Erich W. Zimmermann's INTRODUCTION
TO WORLD RESOURCES

ERICH W. ZIMMERMANN'S

INTRODUCTION TO WORLD RESOURCES

EDITED BY **Henry L. Hunker**
THE OHIO STATE UNIVERSITY

HARPER & ROW, PUBLISHERS
NEW YORK, EVANSTON, AND LONDON

Erich W. Zimmermann's INTRODUCTION TO WORLD RESOURCES

Library of Congress Catalog Card Number: 64–20276

CONTENTS

PREFACE

If there is a classic in the fields of resource economics, conservation, or economic geography, Erich Zimmermann's *World Resources and Industries* is it. The volume has been praised widely by economist, geographer, conservationist, and resource expert alike since it was first published in 1933.

Zimmermann, a distinguished professor of economics, wrote an excellent economic geography. His purpose was perhaps best explained in a short note written on July 31, 1933, to C. C. Huntington, former chairman of the Department of Geography, The Ohio State University. In it he announced the forthcoming publication of the first edition in which he ". . . tried to work out a new synthesis between cultural geography and economics . . ." Indicative of his interest in the two fields was the statement ". . . I am convinced that the teaching of economics, especially in its world wide aspects, can be greatly vitalized by increased attention to geography."

In the Foreword to the first edition, Zimmermann indicated that the book was not an economic geography as that term is generally understood but rather an attempt to bridge the gap between the reality with which geographers are concerned and the theory of resource use with which the economist is concerned. An approach to resource study, therefore, might either be descriptive or functional, as Zimmermann viewed it. He chose the latter even though ". . . the functional method necessarily renders the treatment, especially in the first part, somewhat abstract and speculative . . ." Yet it is this very part of Zimmermann's work that makes it unique. For while the total book is outstanding, it is the functional approach to resources found within the first part of the volume that has stimulated new ideas and new approaches to both the thinking and teaching of resource economics and economic geography.

The purpose of this edition, then, is to present the basic functional approach to resources that is the foundation of the larger study. Within the revised and edited ten chapters presented here —the "Part One" of the earlier editions, essentially—is contained the "abstract and speculative" approach that Zimmermann discussed. This work should find ready use as supplementary reading in economics, geography, conservation, natural resources, and other subjects designed to study and appraise resources and resource use. It might well provide the basis for seminar discussions and for individual reading assignments at the graduate level. Such use in classes provided the incentive for this edition. The bulk of the material found elsewhere in the earlier editions of *World Resources and Industries*, while functional in approach and often unique when compared with the typical text, nonetheless is discussed in many standard texts.

This edition is dedicated to the late Professor Alfred J. Wright in appreciation for his alerting his students to this work, for the enthusiasm with which he discussed the functional approach to resource use, and for his tireless interest in teaching.

Henry L. Hunker

June 1964

Erich W. Zimmermann's INTRODUCTION
TO WORLD RESOURCES

1 MEANING AND NATURE OF RESOURCES

THE NEW RESOURCE CONSCIOUSNESS

Resources are the bases of both security and opulence; they are the foundations of power and wealth. They affect man's destiny in war and peace alike. A world that has not forgotten two World Wars and is worried over the possibility of a third is bound to be a resource-conscious world. Nor is this concern over resources confined to the "military potential" in the narrow sense of the term. For in total war "military potential" comes close to being total potential, and in cold war full employment or something approaching it is a strategic objective of the first order.

Basically, concern over resources is nothing new. Peoples have always wondered where tomorrow's bread would come from. Land hunger is as old as the ages. Access to water and control over certain minerals have been crucial questions throughout human history. And yet, at least so far as the West is concerned, there is something definitely new in contemporary resource consciousness. To understand this one must briefly review the history of economic thought of the past two centuries and bring to mind some important events of the recent past which have affected men's thought on economics in general and on resources in particular.

Economic Thought

Throughout the ages men have lived under social controls, tribal taboos, and tyrannies of various kinds, ranging from those of priests and medicine men to those of military dictators and Machiavellian princes. At times, certain privileged groups enjoyed considerable freedom under the law, as did Roman citizens during the Roman Empire; but the majority of the people lived under more or less rigid control, as slaves, as serfs, as subject peoples.

1

Then with the great discoveries and inventions there came a time of great change. The white race experienced an amazing expansion of opportunities. It was an age of empire building and colonizing, of swarming into wide-open spaces, but it was also an age of new industries and of new and better uses for what nature had to offer. This expansion was accompanied by a growing belief in the rights and powers of the individual. Social controls were loosened both by revolution and by evolution.

In the economic realm this development manifested itself in the gradual abolition of governmental controls over business enterprise, in the belief in laissez faire, in free trade, both internal and external—in short, in what has become known as the free enterprise system. This system, which reached its highest development in the English-speaking world, achieved a tremendous release of individual energies and drives and with it an increase in economic activity and a rise in living standards never before known in the history of man.

This achievement, credited to the removal of social, especially governmental, restraints and the resultant stepping-up of individual zest and performance, gave rise to peculiar ideologies such as the belief in the primacy of economics, especially its superiority over politics, and the doctrine that the best way to promote the public welfare was to let private business entrepreneurs pursue relentlessly their selfish interests. Competition was the force that would bring about the harmonizing of social and private interests.

These ideologies dominated economic thought in the English-speaking world until in the early 1890s Alfred Marshall, in his famous *Principles of Economics,* broke with the laissez-faire school when he refused "to leap the yawning gap between the individual and society," recognized that the relentless pursuit of individual interest did not assure the attainment of the common weal, and proclaimed the need of a deliberate public policy to safeguard public interests. He withdrew the theoretical prop on which economic "harmonics," or the belief in the necessary harmony between individual and group interests, had rested. Marshall's position was supported by other leading theorists such as Pigou and later given far more militant expression by John Meynard Keynes.

One of the main points on which individuals, including private business interests, and the group, represented by the government, differ is in their concern for resources, especially the basic assets such as soil, water, iron, oil, etc. Business as a rule is market-minded, commodity-conscious; its interests are largely limited to the short run. There is a natural tendency to think in terms of the present and the here and to pass off warnings about the hidden or patent impairment of basic assets. Frequently the proper care of these assets—be they the soil, water, and minerals or the health and education of the people—requires programs of unusual range in point of time, the results of which may not be visible for years, perhaps decades, and which in the meantime call for expenditures without corresponding immediate returns. Under such circumstances a business civilization is apt to neglect the care of its basic assets. Unless checked by deliberate interference on behalf of the public interest it is likely to sacrifice them on the altar of immediate profits.

Historical Background of the New Attitude

If it is true, as many believe, that economic theory reflects the general intellectual spirit of the time, one must look to historical developments for the explanation of Marshall's famous declaration of independence from nineteenth-century "harmonics" and its ready acceptance by his contemporaries and successors. What, then, were the historical developments which help to explain this major shift in economic thought? Only a few highlights can be listed, suggestive of further and deeper forces and developments but far from all-inclusive.

Undoubtedly, one of the events which stirred the American people to resource consciousness and with it to a recognition of the fact that business appeared to be neglectful of the basic social assets was the "closing of the frontier" in the sense of the completion of the settlement of the continent, the end of free land. The story of Theodore Roosevelt's eloquent appeal for a conservation policy is too well known to need recounting. It led to a period of pausing in the mad rush, taking stock, and, in a way, locking the stable after the horse was gone. For the first time, people came to realize that even in God's own country the natural endowment of the continent was neither inexhaustible nor indestructible. There was a timid attempt to take inventory. Some reserves showed signs of approaching exhaustion. Even if the practical results were meager, the realization of the finiteness of the national endowment was not wholly smothered by a new "faith in bonanza," the bonanza of technics and science, of mechanical wizardry and chemical magic. This early realization of the exhaustibility of the reserves of the earth's resources has matured into a clearer and more sober understanding of the facts and their meaning.

When the Great Depression led to the New Deal, in the field of resources Franklin Delano Roosevelt took up where Theodore Roosevelt had stopped. The concern over resources was a major one and it was wisely extended to human resources. The National Resources Committee, the National Resources Board, and the National Resources Planning Board, regardless of trivial changes in name, constituted a single force aimed at developing a policy to safeguard our national resources. Alfred Marshall's daring break with the past had borne fruit.

The Great Depression was the last of a series of major economic slumps which more or less had come to be accepted as necessary evils. The severity of this catastrophe, however, brooked no temporizing. Since planning by private corporations had failed dismally, government planning was entitled to a try. One of its chief characteristics, perhaps its most important one, is conscious regard for basic social assets, many—perhaps most—of which lie outside the scope of private business concern. Once the magic spell of the old "harmonics" is broken, the duty to plan for the common good is clear. Unfortunately, where to find the wisdom necessary to perform that duty is another question. Trial and error is a costly, cumbersome method but, as yet, the only one at hand.

Up to this point attention has been focused on spectacular events such as the closing of the frontier, the Great Depression, and the World Wars as sources of growing resource consciousness. They are by no means the only forces responsible for this new awareness. A number of quiet, slowly moving trends have contributed materially to the change in attitude. The growing size and complexity of modern nations is one of them. It points, with perhaps inevitable logic, toward a strengthening of the power of the central government. In so far as this growing complexity is due to a merging of once local or regional activities and interests into national concerns, the connection with increased need for central—in the United States, federal—controls is evident. The growth of the modern corporation is a case in point; there are many others. This trend may be regrettable and beset with grave dangers, but it cannot be conjured away by calling it names. Realities must be faced.

Another equally vital trend is marked by the decline of competition and by its corollary, the concentration of economic power. It is in part coextensive with the growth of the modern corporation and labor union, but it draws attention to particularly ominous aspects of that growth. To appreciate this statement, one must recall that it was reliance on the all-healing power of competition which formed much of the basis of the doctrine of "harmonics." It was through competition and the corresponding absence of monopoly, oligopoly, and other forms of concentrated economic power that the sum total of private interests was assumed to achieve its mystic merging with the public interest, the common good. If nothing else had happened, the decline of competition by itself would insist imperatively upon a public planning policy in which regard for resources, viewed as basic social assets, would be essential.

In other parts of the world far less fortunate than the United States, socialism and communism have brought the virtual disappearance of private enterprise capitalism where it once existed, and precluded its emergence where it has not yet taken root. Both socialism and communism are resource-conscious. Both plan with a view to safeguarding and developing the basic social assets.

Here a fundamental point must be made clear. The fact that both socialism and communism plan does not make planning *ipso facto* socialistic or communistic. The problem is far more complex. The main point to keep in mind is the ultimate objective toward which the planning is directed. If it is directed at safeguarding and strengthening individual rights and views the dignity of the individual human being as the *summum bonum*, it is quite compatible with the highest ideals of democracy. The issue is not whether planning is right or wrong, but how to learn to plan wisely.

A rather subtle influence is what may be called a growing sense of social responsibility. This too helps to explain the increased awareness of the basic social assets. This sense of responsibility is probably best explained in terms of a keener sense of historical perspective and a fuller understanding of social processes and phenomena. It is perhaps a form of enlightened selfishness. Examples of it are Truman's Point IV program on behalf of underdeveloped areas, Nelson Rockefeller's efforts to raise the level of productivity of South American peoples, the enlightened development policy of the United Fruit Company to improve basic assets in the areas in which it operates, and the extensive programs associated with the Peace Corps. All these developments are symptomatic of the growing concern with and for resources. At the same time they cannot help but bring in their train a better understanding of the nature of resources; and this, in turn, is bound to reflect favorably on policies concerning resources.

RESOURCES, AN EVOLVING CONCEPT

Early Misconceptions

The preceding analysis has shown that for centuries resources were the stepchild of economic thought. If they were recognized at all, they were absorbed into the market process, acknowledged only in so far as they were reduced to working tools of the entrepreneur—land, labor, and capital—or recognized through their effects on cost and price, supply and demand.

Being neglected by the economist, the study of resources was left largely to natural scientists, especially physical geographers. It follows that the concept of resources, because it is relatively new, remains to be developed scientifically. A consensus must be achieved among scientists, social as well as natural, as to the exact meaning of the term; and popular misconceptions must be cleared up.

Some of these popular misconceptions may be briefly listed. There is a strong tendency, easily understandable but nonetheless unfortunate, to identify resources with substances or tangible things. To be sure, substances can function as resources, and indeed they play a tremendous part as resources. One has but to think of coal, iron, petroleum, copper, etc., to realize that. They are obvious, easily recognized, and considered important, whereas less patent invisible and intangible aspects—such as health, social harmony, wise policies, knowledge, freedom—are ignored, even though possibly these latter are more important than all the coal, iron, gold, and silver in the world put together. In fact, resources evolve out of the dynamic interaction of all these factors.

Similarly, the preoccupation with so-called natural resources at the expense of human and cultural resources precludes a clear comprehension of the true nature of resources and a full grasp of their extent. Likewise unfortunate is the tendency to think of resources in terms of a single asset, e.g., coal, rather than in terms of the whole complex of substances, forces, conditions, relationships, institutions, policies, etc., which alone help to explain the way coal functions as a resource at a given time and place.

This preoccupation with single tangible phenomena in nature creates the false impression of resources as something static or fixed, whereas actually they are as dynamic as civilization itself. This static concept of resources is well illustrated by the following verse:

> The world is a bundle of hay.
> Mankind are the asses that pull.
> Each tugs it a different way,
> And the greatest of all is *John Bull*.[1]

The concept of the world, the sum total of man's resources, actual and potential, as a bundle of hay is truly fantastic. Hay is dead; it cannot grow; it is used up as it is consumed. No wonder "mankind are the asses that pull," i.e., nations that go to war over what are falsely considered static resources. As the following discussion will bring out, nothing could be further from the truth. Resources are living phenomena, expanding and contracting in response to human effort and behavior. They thrive under rational harmonious treatment. They shrivel in war and strife. To a large extent, they are man's own creation. *Man's own wisdom is his premier resource—the key resource that unlocks the universe.*

Finally, one more popular misconception needs to be brought out: the failure to realize that just as truly as there must be shade when there is light, so also must there be resistances where there are resources. The two words should be inseparable in all resource thinking, just as supply and demand, profit and loss, assets and liabilities are linked together by strong bonds of logic. To help dispel some of these misconceptions is one of the objectives of this analysis.

"Resources" Defined

Dictionary definitions reflect common usage and are therefore

---

[1] This verse is quoted from memory. It was seen by Zimmermann about fifty years ago in London on the cover of a weekly called *John Bull*.

an indication of the meaning generally given to words. It is desirable that scientific usage of common words not depart too far from accepted meanings. Typical dictionary definitions of the word "resources" read as follows:

1. That upon which one relies for aid, support, or supply.
2. Means to attain given ends.
3. The capacity to take advantage of opportunities or to extricate oneself from difficulties.

Evidently resources presuppose a person.[2] They are an expression or reflection of human appraisal. The appraisal finds that something can serve as means to given ends, that one can rely on it for aid, support, or supply. The third definition reveals that resources do not necessarily exist outside the appraiser but can be lodged within him. Evidently there are subjective or internal resources as well as objective or external resources. Subjective resources, furthermore, play a dual role: a positive one of taking advantage of opportunity and a negative one of extricating the individual from difficulties or of overcoming obstacles or resistances.

Our conclusion may be clearly drawn. The word "resource" *does not refer to a thing nor a substance but to a function which a thing or a substance may perform or to an operation in which it may take part,* namely, the function or operation of attaining a given end such as satisfying a want. In other words, the word "resource" is an abstraction reflecting human appraisal and relating to a function or operation. As such, it is akin to such words as food, property, or capital, but much wider in its sweep than any one of these.

Etymologically the word "resource" is related to source. The prefix *re,* meaning "again," suggests dependability through time, as indicated in the word *relies* used in the first dictionary definition. The stress on dependability points toward long-run and social implications, not, however, to the exclusion of other meanings. Here any one of the dictionary definitions listed above could serve satisfactorily. Even better, though, would be a composite of all three. But the emphasis is definitely on basic long-run social assets.

---

[2] One could also speak of the resources of plants and animals. Here the word is restricted to mean the resources at the disposal of persons or groups of persons.

THE FUNCTIONAL OR OPERATIONAL THEORY OF RESOURCES

Resources of man and MAN

The theory of resources developed here is in strict harmony with the functional and operational meaning of the word contained in the above definitions. This theory will now be explained.

The dictionary definitions show that resources result from the interaction between (1) man, searching for means to attain given ends (such as the satisfaction of individual wants and the attainment of group or social objectives) and possessed of the capacity to take advantage of opportunities or to extricate himself from difficulties, and (2) something outside of man which for the time being will be called nature.

To understand resources, one must understand this relationship. For that purpose, it is necessary to conceive of the human being as existing on two levels, the animal level and the *supra*-animal or human (social) level. At this point of the analysis, *man* is used to indicate the former and *MAN* to indicate the latter. *Man* on the animal level constitutes part of nature. *MAN* on the human level represents the counterpart of nature. Nature is non-*MAN*. It is the cosmos in so far as it is unaffected by *MAN*. The sum total of changes wrought by *MAN* is here called culture.

Man, existing without benefit of culture, by virtue of his nature, i.e., his creature wants and his native abilities, is (1) capable of drawing support from nature, e.g., oxygen from the air, water, wild food, situs, etc., and (2) exposed to harmful forces and conditions found in nature, e.g., poison, wild beasts, hostile elements, disease, etc.

Those aspects of nature which *man* can utilize in the satisfaction of his creature wants (without contributions made by *MAN*), may be called natural resources. Those aspects of nature which harm or hinder *man* may be called natural resistances. The extent of want satisfaction is a function of resources *and* resistances, not of resources alone.

Man, i.e., man on the animal level, has only natural wants and natural capacities and therefore he commands only natural resources and is exposed to natural resistances. One can envisage him submerged in an ocean of "neutral stuff," i.e., matter, energy, conditions, relationships, etc., of which he is unaware and which affect him neither favorably nor unfavorably. Immediately surrounding him may be imagined to exist a narrow fringe of natural resources, i.e., aspects favorable to his existence, capable of satisfying his simple creature wants, and limited by the modest range of natural abilities, and natural resistances, i.e., aspects unfavorable or hostile to him.

This animal man was subject to the same laws of ecology and passive adaptation which bind all other animals. His techniques, like all animal techniques, were immutable genus techniques, i.e., techniques identified with and inseparable from the structural and functional characteristics of the genus, an inheritance certain to fall to all normal members of the genus but equally certain never to be improved upon by a single member. Genus techniques are static, unalterable; they are functions of organismic attributes which the organism cannot change at will but which are changed passively under pressure from the environment.

On this animal level man found nature niggardly indeed; he barely managed to survive in the face of resistances which in the absence of cultural aids proved formidable, and on resources which were limited by the scantiness of his own capacities. The race grew slowly, for the death rate was terrific. In fact, for ages the very existence of the race hung in the balance—a situation strangely repeated in the face of the superlative cultural achievements of the atomic age.

Emancipation of MAN

Then there arrived a time, 50,000 or more years ago, when the genus Homo was singled out of all organic creatures to travel a road closed to all others—the road of active man-willed adaptation. *Man,* having learned to stand erect, to use his hand not only to grasp but to make tools, possessing a vocal apparatus of unparalleled plasticity, endowed with physical strength probably greater than that left to us after thousands of years of artificial selection, and with natural brain power probably equal to our own, began his career as the great culture-builder, the powerful earth-changer, the Prometheus who thrusts his hand into the heavens to seize divine power, who, not satisfied with what nature willingly offers, coaxes her to give more, much more, and even imitates her or improves upon her work.

Through his superior brain power, *MAN* has gained control over many of the other creatures found on earth. With its aid he can calculate the future effect of present and future action and can plan accordingly. His plastic vocal apparatus permits the development of articulate speech and with it the all-vital ability to communicate not merely simple impressions but also complex ideas including high-order abstractions. The spoken word is put into writing, into print; permanent records pass on knowledge from generation to generation and from place to place. Thus group relationships are formed, the development of the arts becomes a social process, and culture, the social heritage which feeds upon itself and grows cumulatively through the centuries, emerges to transform the natural landscape.

Thus *MAN* has emancipated himself from the limitations of passive adaptation and natural selection which hold all other creatures in bondage. He learns to make fire, to build shelter; he invents tools, tills the land, domesticates animals, harnesses the inanimate forces of nature and gains dominion over uncounted robot slaves. In short, *MAN* learns to exercise the supreme human prerogative of active adaptation.

His arts are no longer static genus techniques, but dynamic individually invented techniques which benefit from both the spontaneous contributions of countless individuals and the advantages these individuals derive from the all-pervasive social heritage of knowledge and experience.

Paucity of Natural Resources

This story of the rise of man from the animal to the human stage is of the utmost significance for the meaning and nature of *MAN's* resources as distinguished from the resources of animals. *MAN's* resources, to an overwhelming extent, are *not* natural resources. It is true that nature provides the opportunity for *MAN* to display his skill and apply his ever-expanding knowledge. But nature offers freely only an infinitesimal fraction of her treasure; she not only withholds the rest, but seems to place innumerable and, in many cases, well-nigh unsurmountable obstacles in the way of resource-seeking and resource-creating *MAN*.

The majority of *MAN's* resources are the result of human ingenuity aided by slowly, patiently, painfully acquired knowledge and experience. To be sure, coal is found in nature. But coal readily accessible and available for human use is rare indeed. Without the aid of power-driven machinery, human inventions, and man-made contraptions, mankind long ago would have run out of coal. Coal occurs in nature, to be sure, but not coke, or sulfate of ammonia, tar, dyes, aspirin, nylon. All the elements are found in nature; but this is of no value to *man*, who is not even aware of their existence and even less capable of isolating and utilizing them. If there are a hundred elements, there are billions of compounds which can be built up, by commutation and permutation, out of the hundred elements. And only a fraction of them occur in nature.

The Functional Concept of Resources

Wesley C. Mitchell was absolutely correct when he wrote:

> Incomparably greatest among human resources is knowledge. It is greatest because it is the mother of other resources. The aboriginal inhabitants of what is now the United States lived in a poverty-stricken environment. For them no coal existed, no petroleum, no metals beyond nuggets of pure copper. Of electrical energy they had no inkling. Their agriculture was so crude that they could use only tiny patches of the soil. Their rudimentary social organization combined with their ineffective production to keep their groups small and mutually hostile. . . . Not only is knowledge the greatest of resources, it is also the resource that we have counted upon to grow richer with every decade. The cumulative expansion of science and of its practical applications has emboldened us to expect that each generation of our descendants will discover new resources and more efficient ways of using old ones. When the future of mankind was pictured as turning upon the race between science and depletion, most men believed science would win.[3]

Knowledge is truly the mother of all other resources. To be sure, not even omniscience can create matter or energy out of nothing. Nor can any science, no matter how skillful and advanced, ever restore to human use the energy once locked up in coal, oil, or gas, but now spent. The difference between neolithic man, who roamed the earth in misery and fear, and man today, who lives in relative comfort and security, is knowledge and the marvelous apparatus of cultural improvements which knowledge has devised and

[3] See Wesley C. Mitchell, "Conservation, Liberty, and Economics," in *The Foundations of Conservation Education*, National Wildlife Federation, New York, 1941, pp. 1, 2.

built for its own application. Freedom and wisdom, the fruits of knowledge, are the fountainhead of resources.

Seen in this light, the concept of resources is purely functional, inseparable from human wants and human capabilities. It is a concept which legitimately belongs to the social scientist.

The physicist claims that the quantity of matter and energy in the universe is constant; the social scientist replies that nothing is constant, that everything is in flux. In spite of the seeming paradox, both are right. The idea of the fixity of matter and energy in the universe is wholly reconcilable with the claim that resources are in constant flux. The earth is a tiny speck in the vastness of the universe, and mankind, though its numbers may be counted by the billions, is an infinitesimal fraction of that universe. The whole stays put, the fraction forever changes.

Apart from relatively minor changes wrought by man, the earth substantially remains unchanged within the time limits pertinent to mortal man. But its resources change with each change in human civilization. Since geography deals both with the earth as a planet and with the earth as man's abode, it is both a natural science and a social science. Bowman was keenly aware of the implications of this dual role of his science when he wrote:

> It is often said that geography deals with fixed elements because the earth remains substantially the same from generation to generation, its secular changes being slow. Nothing could be further from the truth. . . . The history of societies migrating over and settling in the diverse parts of the earth shows how constant has been the evolution of man's thought about and use of the world. The dark and forbidding mountains of one epoch become the playground and inspiration of another epoch. It has been said that before a thing *is* possible it must *be conceived as* possible. In general, man has done what he thought he could do, and lack of knowledge and the canons of his time have often held him back for long periods. Whenever a new instrument of power or a new chemical discovery or a new use for an old product is discovered the areas affected are reassessed. . . . The geographical elements of the environment are fixed only in the narrow and special sense of the word. *The moment we give them human associations they are as changeful as humanity itself!*[4]

[4] Isaiah Bowman, *Geography in Relation to the Social Sciences,* Charles Scribner's Sons, New York, 1934, pp. 34, 37. (The first italics are Zimmermann's.)

According to Hamilton, "It is technology which gives value to the stuffs which it processes; and as the useful arts advance the gifts of nature are remade. . . . With technology on the march, the emphasis of value shifts from the natural to the processed good."[5]

Those who still insist that the natural environment is constant and that the supply of "land" (i.e., the natural environment) is fixed face a powerful array of opposing authorities.

Nothing is more fatal to a realistic and usable understanding of resources than the failure to differentiate between the constants of natural science and the relatives of social science, between the totality of the universe or of the planet earth, legitimate domain of the natural scientist, and that small portion of these totalities which constitutes the ever-changing resources of a given group of people at a given time and place, the bailiwick of the social scientist.

And somebody had the effrontery to call the world "a bundle of hay"! It is incredible. And others insist to this very day that resources *are*, that they are static and fixed! One has but to consider some of the most precious resources of our age—electricity, oil, nuclear energy—to see who is right, the exponent of the static school who insists that "resources are," or the defender of the dynamic, functional, operational school who insists that "resources become."

Resources and Wants

Resources are dynamic not only in response to increased knowledge, improved arts, and expanding science, but also in response to changing individual wants and social objectives. Resources were defined as means of attaining given ends, i.e., individual wants and social objectives. Means take their meaning from the ends which they serve. As ends change, means must change also. Thus resources must reflect every change in the purpose of the appraiser. The aims of czarist Russia in many ways differed from those of the Soviet Union. The Russian Revolution of 1917 therefore brought on a veritable upheaval of Russian resources. The resources of the United States at war are quite different from those of the United States at peace. They are bound to reflect the change in social objectives. A shift in the national mind from Hamiltonian to Jeffersonian prefer-

---

[5] Walton H. Hamilton, "Control of Strategic Materials," *American Economic Review*, June, 1944, p. 262.

ences, by changing national purposes, must needs change national resources as well.

Nature and Culture

So long as the human race continues to climb upward to higher culture levels, culture is bound to become increasingly important as the dynamic force in the creation of resources. This shift of emphasis toward the cultural by no means implies a disparagement of nature's role and a disregard of physical realities.

> Physical reality at all times is the basis on which human culture rests. The physical environment, appraised both quantitatively and qualitatively and viewed as changing relationships of trends and forces rather than as static conditions, therefore is at all times the foundation of human productive effort. Arts, no matter how highly developed, and wants, no matter how urgent or sophisticated, are helpless in a vacuum. Without acting on and drawing from physical nature they are unproductive. To know, however, what particular opportunities a given physical environment has to offer at a given time and place, one must first learn what man *can* and *wants* to do with it.
>
> *Nature sets the limits within which man can develop his arts to satisfy his wants.* Within these limits he is free to select from the myriad possibilities offered by nature those which at a given time and place promise the best results in terms of want satisfaction in return for the human effort applied thereto. . . . Human culture as a rule is adaptive; that is, it reflects adaptation to natural advantages or disadvantages. Less often it is independently creative, and only in rare cases does it run directly counter to the dictates of nature.[6]

Dynamics of Culture

To appreciate fully the dynamic force of culture, one needs to be aware of the entire scope of its penetrating force. The effects of cultural progress on nature come readily to mind. But cultural influences are not confined to the nonman world; they do not overlook or spare man himself. Not only wants and abilities of the individual man and of groups of men are affected by culture—education, train-

[6] Erich W. Zimmermann, in Walter E. Spahr (ed.), *Economic Principles and Problems,* Holt, Rinehart & Winston, New York, 3rd ed., 1936, vol. 1, pp. 165–166.

ing experience, sophistication, degeneration, eugenics, etc.—but the relationships between men, social organizations, and societal institutions also come under its spell. Groups expand and become more complex; division of labor, regional and occupational, is pushed further. Improved means of communication and transportation bring always wider strata of humanity into contact; contacts grow more frequent and more intimate, and world-wide interdependence results.

Even the size of the human population is apt to be affected by cultural change. The first impact of expanding and improving culture on the numbers of people is rapid increase, even an accelerating rate of increase. But in due time, birth control or "planned parenthood" puts on the brakes. First the rate of increase declines and later the population may suffer an absolute decline.[7]

Culture thus involves a twofold process of change. On the one hand, it comprises the sum total of the cultural modification of the nonman environments, both physical and nonphysical, artifacts as well as arts. On the other hand, it comprises cultural changes affecting human attitudes, human relations within groups as well as between groups. Government, church, trade union, trade association, standards of living, creeds, etc., are all cultural products affecting the human side of the equation.

The Resource Process

The dynamics of resources can be illustrated by diagrams. Of the two that are offered, the first (Fig. 1) shows the simple relationships between primitive man and nature.

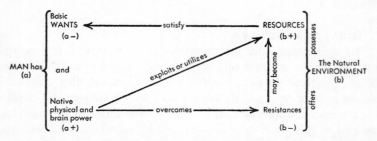

FIGURE 1. Dynamic Interrelationship Between Primitive Man and His Natural Environment

[7] See chap. 8.

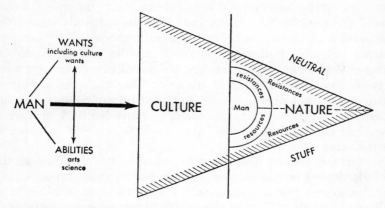

FIGURE 2. Man, Culture, and Nature

It is difficult to depict in a simple diagram the more complex relationships accounting for the resources of man on more advanced levels of civilization. The idea of showing culture as a spearhead which man drives deeper into the realm of nature, converting more and more "neutral stuff" into resources—and into resistances as well —is presented readily enough, as shown in Fig. 2.

But to be satisfactory this diagram should be combined with the first. This, however, would complicate the picture unduly. Moreover, not all cross currents of dynamic interaction would be visible even then—especially the influence of nature on both human wants and the arts and sciences. Something evidently must be left to the reader's imagination.

Destruction of Resources

So far in the discussion of the dynamics of resources, emphasis has been placed on the resource-creating current flowing from man to nature and back again. But not all change is positive, leading to expansion. Man, the great culture-builder, is not only a creator of resources, he is also a destroyer. In part, this destruction is inevitable, a necessary corollary of his use of the earth. Man cannot help that coal and oil are dissipated in use. He cannot use such minerals without using them up. Less obvious is the destruction of resources by man-induced obsolescence. When Kekule, the German chemist, dreamed up the "carbon ring" out of the smoke of his pipe and thus paved the way for the coal-tar industries, he indirectly caused the destruction of entire branches of agriculture, especially those producing vegetable indigo in India and madder root in France. A giant steelworks has no use for little pockets of iron deposits; it must rely on vast accumulations of the stuff. Thus with the advent of modern iron and steel processes, thousands of ore deposits became uneconomical, ceased to be resources, and reverted back to whence they had come—"neutral stuff." One might be tempted to speak of ex-resources.

But far greater destruction is wrought by man not in the orderly process of rational resource use, but because of human folly and cussedness. As was mentioned before, the individual tends to take a short-sighted view of things. He "wants what he wants when he wants it" and as a rule does not reckon the consequences too carefully. What is more, he is apt to ignore, if he can, the consequences for others, especially if the others are as yet unborn. The proper use and care of complex natural processes that are governed by the laws of ecology presuppose a high degree of scientific knowledge which has been reached only very recently, after centuries of blind groping and foolish blundering. Soil erosion caused by faulty methods of farming, of overgrazing, or of unscientific cutting of timber comes readily to mind. So does the careless treatment of water supplies—stream pollution, abuse of rivers, lowering of the water table, etc. The destruction of fauna and flora which interferes with nature's creative work through natural selection and the variation of species limits or even blocks the progress of the plant and animal breeder. Of a similar nature is the wasteful exploitation of minerals. Here again, scientific progress offers many remedies but does not wholly remove the problem of conflicts between short-run individual and long-run group interests.

Another source of trouble, interfering with orderly programs and often causing heavy losses of resource values, if not their outright destruction, is the growing complexity of the social order. As nations increase in size, as economies become more elaborate, and as global interdependence grows, the task of "living together well," of good neighborliness, of The Good Society, grows more difficult and the pitfalls become more numerous and deeper. Perhaps more resources are destroyed or left unborn by class struggle, internal strife, and, above all, by war, than by all other causes put together.

Examples of Resource Creation and Destruction

Thus far, this discussion of resources has been stated in rather theoretical terms. Theoretical abstractions are hard to grasp unless examples from life are cited to bring the analysis down to earth, as it were.

It is easy to find illustrations that verify the functional or operational theory, support the claim that "resourceship" evolves out of the three-way interaction of natural, human, and cultural assets, and prove that natural resources are rare indeed.

For various reasons, Latin America is a region where the processes of resource development and disappearance are unusually transparent. The examples that follow are chosen from recent Latin-American history.[8]

Rubber from the Amazon region had been known to people in the western hemisphere for centuries, but little could be done with it until Charles Goodyear discovered vulcanization in 1839. As a result of his discovery, rubber could be used to satisfy essential human wants. Business concerns soon sprang up to manufacture and sell articles made of vulcanized rubber. The difference between the processing costs and what the purchasers of these articles were willing to pay set the price the traders could pay for rubber in its native state. This price in turn determined how many natives could be hired to gather it from trees that grew wild in the jungles of the Amazon basin and prepare it for the market; i.e., this price determined the extent of the areas that were worth tapping. In short, the demand of people throughout the world for vulcanized rubber goods governed the process by which "neutral stuff" in the wilds of the Amazon could be converted into the rubber resources of Brazil.

The importance of Goodyear's invention should not be overlooked. For, in this age of machine industry and science, it is the inventor and after him the technologist who usually open up the opportunity for the risk-taking businessman to set the actual resource-creating process in motion. But in its entirety, the resource-

[8] Based on Erich W. Zimmermann, "Resources of Latin America, a Study in Methodology."

creating setup is composed of many parts—invention and technology, business enterprise, market demand, labor, capital equipment, and the social and political institutions governing international trade and regulating human relationships both *intra*nationally and *inter*nationally. Not only are all these parts essential, but there must be the proper balance between them.

Another example of resource creation is to be found in the iron deposits of Minas Gerais in Brazil. These deposits, among the largest in the world, have been known for a long time. But it has been only within the past quarter century that a truly modern industry using this iron has developed. Among the reasons for the delay were the inaccessibility of the inland deposits and the lack of nearby coking coal with which to smelt the ore.

To achieve the conversion of this iron from "neutral stuff" to resource, several things were necessary: (1) international cooperation, initially in the form of the Good Neighbor Policy between the United States and Brazil, which reflected political interests and peoples' attitudes, and the understanding that existed between their governments; (2) capital, in the form of credit and mechanical equipment and know-how; (3) a domestic market for Brazilian-made steel products, subsidized by a government anxious to own its steelworks and willing to pay the cost differential between Brazilian production and the world market price; (4) a foreign market for iron ore created by World War II; (5) able and willing labor and its impact upon labor legislation, wage policies, and social security; (6) modern sanitation to make the fever-ridden valley to the port of Vitoria livable; and (7) modern technology, which performed one miracle after another along the line from ore to blast furnace to Siemens converter to Koppers coke oven.

This story could be told over and over again. It has many variations, but the theme is always the same. Resourceship stems from the purposeful interaction of natural, cultural, and human factors primed and kept going by demand based on availability for use.

But there is another side to the story. The process can be reversed. Not only do modern science and technology backed by wants and needs create resources; they also destroy them and reconvert them into "neutral stuff." Again, Brazilian rubber is a good example. When the possibilities of the rubber tire were first recognized, it became apparent that the supply of wild rubber would be both inadequate in amount and too costly; in short, it would constitute a bottleneck in the rubber goods industry in general and in the tire industry in particular. The establishment of rubber plantations in Southeast Asia—Ceylon, the Malay Peninsula, the Netherlands East Indies (now Indonesia)—was the answer. With the aid of genetics, the European owners succeeded in breeding new varieties of rubber trees infinitely more productive than the wild trees of the jungle. Thus, cost was brought down to a mere fraction of the Brazilian figure, and the daughter industry squeezed the mother industry out of the world market. The application of modern science and technology to the development of synthetic rubber has had its impact upon the rubber industry of Southeast Asia as well. It is but a continuing example of man's ability to create and destroy resources.

All these examples prove the same basic fact: *resources are not, they become;* they are not static, but expand and contract in response to human wants and human actions. In these examples, two forms of human action were prominent: technics and business enterprise. But other forms of human action at times become determinant as resource makers or destroyers, overshadowing the influence of the inventor and the entrepreneur. One of the most important of these is *governmental policy.* Reference to the petroleum industry in two Latin American countries will illustrate this point.

Mexico was the first of the countries in which, soon after the turn of the century, a large modern petroleum industry was developed. In 1921, Mexican exports amounted to over one-fifth of the world crude oil output. But after World War I, the output curve went into a tailspin as the big oil companies, whose Mexican properties had been taken over by a revolutionary government, turned from Mexico to Venezuela. In less than 20 years, Venezuela, with a more favorable government attitude toward foreign investment, surpassed Mexico's peak output figure.

To understand more fully this account of the oil industry, keep in mind the following facts: (1) the exploitation of oil fields, especially in the tropics, requires vast amounts of capital; (2) the markets for both crude oil and refined products are outside of Latin America; (3) it is generally the advanced industrialized countries that have the technical know-how and the general scientific background required; (4) under these circumstances, most Latin-American oil fields can be developed on a large scale and an efficient basis only by foreign capital; (5) therefore, foreign oil companies that are willing to risk their capital here require reasonable assurance that their investments will be safe from unpredictable and irresponsible political interference; and (6) consequently, *laws, political attitudes, and government policies,* along with basic geological and geographical facts, become the strategic factors in determining which oil fields will be converted by foreign capital from useless "neutral stuff" into the most coveted resource of modern times.

Resources—Where the Sciences Meet

Both the analysis that preceded and the examples just cited make clear that the study of resources belongs in the field of the social sciences, but that the synthesizing work of the social scientist must rest on the findings of both natural and applied scientists. The field of the social sciences is wide indeed. It embraces history, sociology, cultural anthropology, economics, government, etc. The fields of the natural and applied sciences are even wider. The study of resources thus inevitably becomes the study of synthesis. If such synthesis is not to bog down in confusion and shallowness, the field must be carefully surveyed and blocked out. This will be attempted.

Since the resources at the disposal of man evolve out of the working combination of natural, human, and cultural aspects—a combination which expands with every advance of human knowledge and wisdom and contracts with every relapse into the barbarism of war and civil strife—the study of resources logically falls into separate phases or divides into separate fields:

1. The study of the materials, energies, living organisms, conditions, etc., found in nature.
2. The study of man, on the animal as well as on the supra-animal level, viewed both individually and in society.
3. The study of human culture in all its aspects, including technology, social and political institutions, its history, nature, trends, etc.
4. The study of the interrelations between these three fields.[9]

[9] This list is restricted to studies *directly* concerned with resources. Since all scientific effort rests on fundamentals contained in mathematics, logic, philosophy, pure science, etc., these too must be considered, though their contributions are *indirect.* Likewise, the tools of communication—alphabet, numbers, symbols, language, etc.—should not be overlooked.

Such a study of resources calls for the services of:

1. The physical or natural sciences, including anatomy, physiology, histology, psychology, biology, zoölogy, bacteriology, botany, ecology, geology, physical geography, climatology, pedology, physics, chemistry, mechanics, etc. The function of these sciences is to reveal what is, where it is, why it is, how it is, how different segments interact, etc. Their study is purely objective, i.e., wholly detached from the human viewpoint. Their exponents are primary fact-finders of society.

2. The "applied" scientists: the engineer, the economic geologist, the human or economic geographer, the industrial chemist, the surgeon, physician, public health expert, etc. They are the technicians of society. They determine what is *technically feasible*. They apply the knowledge gathered by the fact-finders and the "pure" scientists.

3. The entrepreneurs who lend financial support to those applications of science and techniques which to them appear profitable. They narrow the field of the technically feasible by applying additional tests of feasibility. To the technician's question, "Is it technically feasible?" they add the question, "Is it financially profitable?"

4. Economists who further narrow the choice of action by asking, "What is best for society in the long run?" Their supreme task in society is that of helping to shape the grand strategy of the utilization of all resources with a view to maximizing the social benefits derived from the most effective, best, or wisest use of "scarce means applied to alternate ends." In this difficult task the economist is aided by all social scientists who throw light on the nature, structure, and function of society.

In brief, the natural scientist deals with "neutral stuff," with things *per se*. All the others evaluate and choose. The applied scientist separates the feasible from the nonfeasible or the not-yet-feasible. The businessman seeks to differentiate the profitable from the unprofitable, or the more profitable from the less profitable. The social "scientist" tries to distinguish between good and evil, between that which promotes the common good and that which harms.

One might summarize the functions of these four groups in terms of the questions which each seeks to answer:

1. What is? Where is it? How is it and why? How does it behave and why?
2. What can we do with it?
3. How should it be used to yield the highest return to private enterprise?
4. How should it be used to yield the highest return to society?

It is evident from the foregoing that no one group can, by itself, fully understand and appraise resources. Such an understanding and appraisal are joint responsibilities. The appraisal of resources proceeds from:

1. The knowledge of facts of nature and culture to
2. the determination of technical feasibility to
3. the determination of profitability to
4. the formulation of the grand strategy along socio-economic lines.[10]

Stages 3 and 4 involve subjective evaluation. They lack the advantage of scientific objectivity characteristic of Stages 1 and 2.

In reality, these categories are seldom if ever as clearly distinguished as this oversimplified exposition makes it appear. Much of the work in the social sciences, such as statistics and history, is of a fact-finding, data-collecting nature, and there is no reason why the natural scientist and the applied scientist may not look beyond the physical facts and rules of technical feasibility to the ultimate social implications of their findings and work. In fact, there is good reason why they should!

Two sets of interdependent criteria may be distinguished in the appraisal of resources:

1. *The State of the Wants,* the expression of human needs, individual wants, social objectives, higher aspirations.
2. *The State of the Arts,* as the summation of human capacities along lines of both technology and social organization.

The constant flux in which these two sets of criteria exist communicates itself to the resources to the appraisal of which these criteria apply. While the physical universe may be constant, while the planet earth may undergo few changes speedy and substantial enough to affect materially the destiny of man, the resources available to the human race are in constant flux, changing reflections of changing capacities and needs.[11]

Synopsis

The presentation of the functional or operational theory of re-

[10] During the nineteenth century in the English-speaking world the belief was widely held that the determination of profitability automatically took care of socio-economic strategy. That belief has been badly shaken and is now shared by only a small minority.

[11] Erich W. Zimmermann, "Resources—an Evolving Concept," *Transactions, Texas Academy of Science, 1944,* September 1945.

sources is inevitably complex. Roaming over wide areas of thought, one is apt to lose the thread and fail to see the forest because of the trees. The various points discussed in this chapter, therefore, are brought to a focus in a single table. This table brings out the trinity of natural, cultural, and human aspects from which resourceship evolves; it views them as means (instrumental wealth) to ends (real wealth); it recognizes the presence of resistances, the overcoming of which absorbs a large portion of instrumental wealth, leaving only a residual ("net resources") for the promotion of real wealth. These basic concepts are elaborated by breaking down both resources and resistances into various subdivisions and by implementing the concept of real wealth with slogans and a quotation.

TRENDS IN RESOURCE DEVELOPMENT

Table 1 may give a false impression of a one-way flow from top to bottom, from means to ends. As was pointed out, the process is not one-way. The current flows from ends to means with equal ease. In the same way it is difficult to state when and how far man initiates the process of resource development with nature the passive factor, and when and how far nature takes the lead in coaxing, urging, perhaps even compelling man to action.

If it is difficult to determine the source of the movement, it is almost impossible to determine its direction. Studying the western world during the past few centuries, one may be inclined to view the movement as following an ascending spiral. Wants multiply, arts improve, ever higher tiers of cultural improvements are superimposed on the natural foundations.

Yet while changed or expanding wants create new resources, others are destroyed. Progress always means a net gain but seldom a pure gain. Creating the better, we must often destroy the good. Moreover, a study of all cultures past and present may lead one to a less optimistic interpretation. One gets the impression of waves rising and falling, of ebb and flow. Perhaps each successive tidal wave reaches a little higher than its predecessor and each successive ebb does not fall back as far as the preceding one. Philosophers do not agree. They do not all anticipate the Decline of the West with the fatalism of a Spengler.

TABLE 1. Resources, Resistances and End Values[a]

Natural Aspects ("Land")	Cultural Aspects ("Capital")	Human Aspects ("Labor")
RESOURCES OR MEANS (Instrumental Wealth)		
I. Factors of Production		
a. *Primary or Original*		
Free gifts of nature.	. . . .	Native abilities and drives.
	b. *Secondary or Derived*	
Aspects of nature which become available for use by man as a result of improvements made by man—improvements in nature as well as in himself.	Instruments of, and aids to, production such as tools, engines, machines, factories, residences, cities, ports, canals, railroads, highways, dams, power lines, cables, telephone and telegraph lines, radio, television, irrigation, drainage, improved strains of useful plants and animals, improved soils, surplus funds, etc.	Human capacities developed through education, training, experience, improved health, etc.
II. Conditioning Factors		
a. *Primary or Original*		
Aspects of nature such as climate, topography, location, configuration, etc., in so far as their conditioning force is unaffected by man.	. . . .	Social attitudes, favorable to "living together."
	b. *Secondary or Derived*	
The same conditioning aspects of nature listed above in so far as their conditioning force is affected by man.	Facilitating agencies of commerce and finance; social institutions such as government (law and order, justice, public health, postal service, etc.), church, school, mores, state of the industrial arts, credit, accumulated knowledge, ethics, level of morals, etc.	Constructive labor attitudes, management attitudes, labor-management relations, aspirations.

TABLE 1. Resources, Resistances and End Values (Cont.)

Natural Aspects ("Land")	Cultural Aspects ("Capital")	Human Aspects ("Labor")
	RESISTANCES	
	I. Direct Obstacles	
	a. *Primary or Original*	
Catastrophes such as storms, floods, tidal waves, earthquakes, pestilence, drought, insect pests, disease, poisonous plants and animals, etc.	. . . .	Human failings such as "cussedness," lack of foresight, mismanagement, failure to comprehend complexities and multiple correlations; ignorance, stupidity, greed.
	b. *Secondary or Derived*	
Denuded mountainsides, erosion, silted and polluted streams and harbors, depleted mineral reserves, lost strains of fauna and flora, ecological disturbances, etc.	"Bad capital" resulting from miscalculation or erroneous appraisal; obsolete equipment not yet written off, etc.	Human difficulties resulting from the complexities of modern industrial civilization; warped judgment; "false Messiahs."
	II. Indirect Handicaps	
	a. *Primary or Original*	
Distance, topographical and locational obstacles, unfavorable distribution of raw materials and energy sources, climatic handicaps, etc.	. . . .	Population densities below or above the "optimum," unfortunate distribution of population relative to changing opportunities, age composition unfavorably affecting productivity.
	b. *Secondary or Derived*	
The handicaps listed above in so far as they are aggravated by cultural impacts.	"The dead hand of the past," vested rights, threats from stronger neighbors causing diversion of instrumental wealth into unproductive channels; business cycles, depressions; abortive policies.	Racial conflicts; class struggle; war.

TABLE 1. Resources, Resistances and End Values (Cont.)

OBJECTIVES OR END VALUES (Real Wealth)

"Life, Liberty, and the Pursuit of Happiness"

Atlantic Charter . . . "The Four Freedoms" . . . Philadelphia Manifesto

Liberty, Security, and Human Decency

"The only *final* value is human life, or rather human living, with all its richness and fullness of experience. This, I take it, is what Ruskin meant when he exclaimed, 'There is no wealth but life!' The *intrinsic* values comprise the things which constitute the positive content of living, the things we desire for their own sake—work and play, love and friendship, hearth and home, and so on, together with such general conditions as peace, security, liberty, and opportunity. The huge class of *instrumental* values includes all our material wealth of whatever kind, all our technological knowledge, all government, and all the economic processes of production and exchange. In fact *all* social institutions belong in this category of instrumental values—*means* to something nearer to the heart of man."

ALBERT B. WOLFE

Presidential address delivered at the Fifty-sixth Annual Meeting of The American Economic Association, Washington, D.C., January 21, 1944, published in *The American Economic Review*, Vol. XXIV, Number One, March, 1944, p. 2.

^a Erich W. Zimmermann, "What We Mean by Resources," in *Texas Looks Ahead*, vol. 1 of *The Resources of Texas*, University of Texas, Austin, 1944.

BIBLIOGRAPHY

Barnett, Harold J. and Chandler Morse, *Scarcity and Growth, The Economics of Natural Resource Availability*, Baltimore: The Johns Hopkins Press (for Resources for the Future), 1963.

Clark, Colin, *The Conditions of Economic Progress*, New York: St. Martin's Press, 3rd ed., 1957.

Fairgrieve, James, *Geography and World Power*, New York: E. P. Dutton & Company, Inc., 8th ed., 1941.

Firey, Walter, *Man, Mind, and the Land*, New York: The Free Press of Glencoe, 1960.

Galbraith, John K., *Economic Development in Perspective*, Cambridge: Harvard University Press, 1963.

Hoover, Calvin, *The Economy, Liberty, and the State,* New York: Twentieth Century Fund, 1959.

Jarrett, Henry (Ed.), *Perspectives on Conservation,* Baltimore: The Johns Hopkins Press (for Resources for the Future), 1958.

Land, Yearbook of Agriculture, 1958, Washington, D.C.: United States Department of Agriculture, 1958.

Mouzon, Olin T., *International Resources and National Policy,* New York: Harper & Row, Publishers, Inc., 1959.

Pounds, Norman J. G., *Political Geography,* New York: The McGraw-Hill Book Company, Inc., 1963.

Smith, Guy-Harold (Ed.), *Conservation of Natural Resources,* New York: John Wiley & Sons, Inc., 1958.

Thomas, William L., Jr. (Ed.), *Man's Role in Changing the Face of the Earth,* Chicago: The University of Chicago Press (for the Wenner-Gren Foundation for Anthropological Research and The National Science Foundation), 1956.

Udall, Stewart L., *The Quiet Crisis,* New York: Holt, Rinehart & Winston, Inc., 1963.

Ward, Barbara, *The Rich Nations and the Poor Nations,* New York: W. W. Norton and Company, 1962.

2 RESOURCE APPRAISAL: HUMAN WANTS AND SOCIAL OBJECTIVES

The word "resource" has been called a term of appraisal. It reflects human judgment as to want-satisfying capacity or utility. The appraisal seeks to determine whether an aspect of the environment provides or supports or serves as a source of supply of desirable goods and services. Appraisal, therefore, is at the heart of the resource process. It will be scrutinized in this chapter and the next.

NATURE AND CULTURE WANTS; STANDARDS OF LIVING

Human wants may be divided into two groups: *basic,* or natural, creature, or existence wants, and *culture* wants. Basic wants must be satisfied if the life of the individual and of the group is to go on. They vary according to age, sex, mode of life, habitat, individual constitution, and, perhaps, also according to racial characteristics. Basic wants can be divided into positive and negative wants. Man needs food, air, and water to build up or maintain bones, tissues, and blood, and to support the vital processes. These are positive wants. He must ward off cold and disease and protect himself against attack. Hence shelter, clothing, armor, etc., may be said to satisfy negative wants. These basic wants are the starting point of the economic process and consequently of resource appraisal. They found early expression in the eloquent language of tribal custom, worship, and the ceremonies of primitve peoples. Sun, light, fire, mother earth, and a father spirit who sends fertilizing rain were the central ideas of ancient religious cults.

But human desires seldom, if ever, stop when basic wants are satisfied. Man tends to eat and drink more than is absolutely necessary for mere existence. He craves variety and adds touches of refinement to the form and content of basic want satisfaction. A taste for the beautiful develops. Bright colors, luster, and sheen hold a primitive appeal. Thus to the basic wants are added more refined and sophisticated desires. To the basic or nature wants are added culture wants.

Individual wants, through established habit and social sanction, tend to crystallize into group *standards of living*. Once such standards have become established, any force which threatens to lower them is fiercely resisted. The peoples of the earth differ widely in living standards, and hence in their appraisal of a given environment. A plot of land may yield a Japanese family a living which to them appears bounteous; it may yield a fair living to a Russian family, and no living at all to a family of native Americans. Living standards involve the idea of leisure. Under one standard man may expect nothing but hard work from sunrise to sunset without greater reward than the bare necessities of life; under another, he may complain if six hours' labor does not yield a liberal margin over and above these necessities.

Wants and Want Doctrines

The crystallization process goes farther. Besides standards of living—that is, of wants—there develop doctrines about wants. These doctrines may be divided into negative or want discouragement doctrines—such as asceticism—and positive or want encouragement doctrines. In the past, civilizations seem to have possessed a limited driving force, and when this was spent, they have tended to stagnate, to become static. The natural tendency of wants to expand and of standards of living to push upward must then be checked. Under such conditions an attitude of resignation tends to develop. Such an attitude is prevalent among some primitive societies. Among more sophisticated peoples it may take the form of a conscious doctrine, a philosophy of want discouragement, of asceticism. The ascetic seeks happiness in self-denial, in the suppression or curtailment of wants. Whether he finds what he seeks is another question.

This negative attitude toward human wants, this ascetic doctrine, is found among some of the overpopulated countries of the East where material arts seem to have reached the limit of spontaneous improvement. Traces of this ascetic doctrine are also found during many periods of human history and in many places on the earth. In his fascinating book on Mexico, Stuart Chase tells the story of a European salesman who despairs of the "damned wantlessness" of the Indians. The enthusiasm of the Germans for oriental philosophy after their defeat in World War I is another case in point.

The opposite doctrine may be called the positive philosophy of want encouragement. It rests on the belief that material progress leads to happiness, and that progress, in turn, depends on want expansion and want multiplication. In its extreme form this modern doctrine is found in North America today. The American variant is marked by an inadequate differentiation between wants spontaneously developing in the course of social evolution and wants artificially created and imposed upon the consuming masses, not in response to organic changes in tastes and desires but in response to technical developments of factory production and corporate management, manifesting themselves in stupendous advertising campaigns.[1] This extreme development found in North America is the culmination of a long line of changes which were set in motion by the Crusades, which re-established the contact of temperate-zone Europe with the East, by the great discoveries, by the Renaissance, but above all, by the Industrial Revolution. So important has this conscious expansion and multiplication of wants become in modern capitalistic industry that Rathenau goes so far as to call the modern entrepreneur "the creator of new wants."

The Nature of Wants

Because of its far-reaching economic significance, a difference in the nature of basic and culture wants must here be mentioned. As has been said, basic wants must be satisfied if life is to go on. Nature demands a minimum of satisfaction up to which nature wants not only rank first in urgency, but simply must be met. Nature, however, sets not only a definite minimum, but also a maximum. A hard-working adult cannot long remain healthy and strong without a minimum daily food intake of 2000 calories, nor can he long remain fit if he regularly consumes more than 5000 calories a day. Room temperatures in the temperate zone should not fall below 65 degrees for any considerable length of time, nor should they ex-

---

[1] The effect of such advertising upon society is the general theme of two books by Vance Packard, *The Hidden Persuaders* and *The Waste-Makers*.

ceed 75 degrees. More or less, all elementary wants are subject to this law of absolute limitations. This is their most important characteristic.

Another feature should be mentioned. Elementary wants are generally recurring. Soon after being stilled, appetite develops anew. We ordinarily require about eight hours' rest out of every twenty-four. Thus basic wants may be said to be recurrent and hence relatively constant.

Culture wants differ in both respects, for they are neither subject to minima or maxima set by nature, nor are they constant or recurring. To be sure, the consumer habits of individuals, which, as stated above, tend to crystallize into standards of living, may develop to such a degree of intensity that physiological dispensables become psychic necessities. Conspicuous consumption plays its part, as in the case of automobiles and homes; social prestige or "caste" may establish consumption minima. Sex appeal must also be considered. Nevertheless, as a rule, culture wants are not quite as insistent in the lower ranges of consumption, nor is a saturation point reached as soon, or as certainly, as in the case of basic wants. This difference in the nature of wants is of vital importance in resource appraisal.

INDIVIDUAL WANTS AND SOCIAL OBJECTIVES

The wants of the individual are the foundation of all resource appraisal; but they are not all, for man seldom lives alone, a hermit, in utter isolation. Group life promotes efficiency and security. In the opinion of some observers, the social instinct is a definite part of human nature. The resource appraisal of the environment, therefore, must be enlarged or modified to take these social wants or objectives into account. Want satisfaction broadens into the attainment of social objectives. The environment must not only yield that which satisfies individual wants, but serve as the reliable basis of continued group life.

Resource appraisal—that is, the appraisal of the usefulness of the environment to man—must therefore be studied from two different angles: first, from the standpoint of individual human wants, and second, from that of social objectives. Hence the question as to what forces control this division and delimit the provinces of private choice and of social control, of individual rights and liberties and of group power, respectively, assumes vital importance.

Group interests or social wants do not replace individual interests or private wants. They never can; for, after all, a group consists of individuals who must eat, drink, sleep, keep warm, and so on. Group interests supplement private wants. In a society limited by inadequate natural opportunities, social wants may encroach on private wants; but where the natural foundation of civilization is wide and firm, the satisfaction of social wants and the safeguarding of group interests are apt to result in a fuller life for the individual. Group cooperation may so stimulate and accelerate creative effort that not only group interests but also the wants of individuals are better served. In an ideal society, the attainment of social objectives is assumed to result in a fuller satisfaction of individual wants, for social aims and individual wants, in theory at least, run parallel toward the same goal. Cooperation in organized groups is essentially a device of collective want satisfaction. In reality, however, the social and private interests frequently clash in head-on collision. This is due to various reasons, some of which will be discussed.

Conflict Between Private and Social Interests

Team play is based on give-and-take. In a football game the individual player voluntarily forgoes a modicum of self-determination of action in order to improve, through better cooperation, the chances of success for his team. If team play pays, the players are rewarded for their sacrifice of self-determination with surer and greater victories. Man soon discovered that security could best be assured by group cooperation. Thus defense became a major, if not the primary, function of government. As groups grew in size, as life —both individual and group life—became more complex, the advantages of team play became less evident and the benefits of give-and-take between individual and group less manifest. Sacrifices demanded of the individual by the group in the interest of group safety were often resented.

Defense is not the only function generally delegated by individuals to the group. The guardianship over public health and internal peace are other basic tasks entrusted to group management, if we may apply this term to government. We tend to go farther, for, on the ground that defense, health, and internal peace rest most securely on wealth and prosperity, the group becomes the champion of economic progress. As such, it may at times have to interfere with individual liberty, and consequently friction results.

This cannot surprise anyone who is at all familiar with the complexity of modern social organization. The most important social group of modern times is the state. Within it may be found innumerable social relationships, such as the family in both the narrow and broader sense, churches, lodges, trade associations, the Red Cross, D.A.R., sanitary districts, political parties, academies, the American Legion, and so forth. These form a complicated pattern of organization and cross-organization, of the grouping and regrouping of individuals for specific purposes and for the pursuit of varied interests—social, political, economic, and eleemosynary.

These associations, in turn, may project their activities and affiliations beyond state boundaries as in the case of the Catholic Church, international cartels, or the Rotary Club; or they may form partisan or particularistic blocs within the state, such as the farm bloc or the Grand Army of the Republic, and so forth. Relationships may develop formally or informally among the states, such as the International Postal Union, the World Court, the United Nations, the European Economic Community (Common Market), or the Communist Bloc. But, on the other hand, definite rivalries may also develop, for this complexity of social groupings creates friction, causes misunderstanding, and renders difficult the proper correlation between group needs and individual wants.

The diversity of attitudes and objectives threatens to turn resource appraisal into something akin to a Chinese puzzle. It is difficult to find one's way in this modern maze of loyalties—and yet good citizenship has been aptly defined as the "right ordering of all our loyalties."

Modern Man a Bundle of "Egos"

Modern man may be thought of as made up of many "egos." According to which "ego" happens to dominate at a given moment, he will arrive at very different conclusions in the resource appraisal of his environment. An example will make this clearer. A man is appraising a parcel of real estate; he is a realtor, the father of children, the chairman of the playground committee of his community, and a member of a committee appointed by the President of the United States to study national problems of land utilization. According to the particular capacity in which he thinks, speaks, and acts at a given moment, he will hold widely different opinions and, perhaps, advocate different policies concerning the plot of ground in question.

This example is typical, and it goes to show that the average man in western civilization lives his life partly as a private individual, and partly as a member of some social group. As a private individual he seeks to satisfy his natural craving for creature comforts and to bring to realization his personal hopes and ambitions; he works for his family or for himself and in general follows his own wishes and interests. But as a citizen of his town or village, state or country, he finds that he must, to some extent, sacrifice his personal freedom and "play the game." How the individual adjusts to this conflict of interests—in other words, how he "orders his loyalties"—is largely a sociological problem. Here we are interested in its resource aspects. In this connection, the term "the three economies" has been used; they are described as follows:

> On the basis of this relationship of the individual to the group, economic life may be divided into three phases: At one extreme are numerous activities left entirely to individual initiative and private enterprise; at the other extreme are activities such as the administration of justice and the provisions for the armed forces which are generally conceded to be matters of public or social concern. Between these two extremes there lies a "third economy" where the balance between private interest and social concern is not as readily determined, and where boundary lines are blurred. This "third economy" comprises, among other activities, extractive natural-resource industries such as mining and lumbering (the latter unless on a sustained-yield basis). The extent to which the State should interfere in private business is most debatable with regard to such activities affecting vital group assets. The power industry is another case in point. To a lesser extent even agriculture lies within the domain of this "third economy." For even soil fertility can become a wasting asset through abuse.
>
> Nations differ widely with regard to their attitudes toward this middle zone. Some nations practically absorb it into the province of free individual enterprise, leaving to social control only a narrow fringe of public functions. Other nations take the very opposite attitude. Such differences in attitude are explained partly by his-

torical forces which have molded national character, partly by differences in the actual situation which these nations are facing at a given time. Difference in pressure brought to bear on groups either from the outside, perhaps by hostile neighbors, or from the inside, possibly by underprivileged and restive classes, seems to account for much of the differences between national attitudes toward the control over this "third economy."[2]

Class Conflict and Social Objectives

In a utopian world all people are striving toward "the greatest good for the greatest number" and promoting the social welfare. In reality, however, social organizations, and hence social objectives, fall far short of such an ideal. At best, a modern group rests on a compromise between conflicting interests as, for instance, the interests of producers and consumers, capitalists and wage earners, country and city, agriculture and manufacturing industries, etc. Such a compromise is seldom so fair as to prove permanent or to stop the grumbling of the discontented. Thus, change is the rule rather than the exception, and internal strife is often merely stifled by force instead of being removed by equitable adjustment. In reality, the so-called group interest may not be much more than the interest of a dominant class parading in the cloak of social necessity, and national policy may aim at the social objectives of a class or a combination of classes rather than at the fullest satisfaction of the most urgent wants of the greatest number.

Groups differ materially as to the manner in which benefits and privileges are distributed among their members. In czarist Russia the beneficiaries or privileged classes constituted barely more than 10 percent of the population. In ancient Greece, free men usually formed a minority. Privileges generally develop as a result of initial superior strength—physical, political, and economic. This may lead to a compromise between strong and weak, the weak assuming certain burdens in return for a guarantee of security from the strong. However, such a compromise may survive its usefulness, for the strong sometimes become the privileged class and wish to retain their privileges long after the need for protection has ceased.

The intensity of the conflict between group and individual, be-

[2] Erich W. Zimmermann, in Walter E. Spahr (ed.), *Economic Principles and Problems*, Holt, Rinehart & Winston, New York, 3rd ed., 1936, vol. 1, p. 186.

tween social and private interests, depends in the first place on the equity of group organization or, to be more specific, on the equity with which duties and rights, sacrifices and benefits are adjusted. Man functions in the resource scheme in the dual capacity of agent and beneficiary, as producer and consumer. Social order rests largely on the proper coordination of these two functions. In a nation which is so rich that, in spite of a not entirely equitable division of benefits, even the least fortunate have enough or can "make a decent living," the question of an equitable distribution of rights and duties is not apt to have as strong a claim on people's thoughts as it does in poorer nations. Again, the sense of social justice is not equally developed in all people. Some may vegetate in sodden poverty almost unaware of their own misery; others are quick to resent any departure from their conception of fair play. As a rule, the more highly civilized people tend to belong to the second class. It may be safe to assume also that the sense of social justice is more highly developed today than it was in antiquity.[3]

Hence this conflict is connected with the question of national prosperity or wealth. National wealth depends, in the first place, on the natural environment itself, on the availability—or utility—of the untransformed aspects of nature. It depends, in the second place, on the arts and institutions to which that environment, in view of the racial and cultural characteristics of the human element, gives rise. Among these, the institutions surrounding population increase are of special importance, for the largess of nature may result either in an ever-growing number of people at or near a point of minimum sustenance, or in a rising living standard for a restricted number. It is a popular belief that the savage is relatively free. This is not strictly true, for the rules of primitive tribal life are ironclad, and ceremonial duties can press as heavily on the savage as conflicting loyalties may weigh on us. Potentially, at least, every improvement in the technique of production and in the social order means the increase of individual liberty.

Prosperity and Security as Social Objectives

In addition to the social and economic aspects, the political

[3] The wave of nationalism that has swept Africa and created many new, independent African nations, and the determined move toward equality by the American Negro are cases in point.

factor must be considered. Referring to this question, Seely, the English historian, went so far as to say: "The amount of freedom that may reasonably exist in a state is in inverse proportion to the military-political pressure exerted by foreign states against its boundaries."[4] This statement may well be expanded to cover the internal dangers as well. It suggests what one may term a pressure theory of social order. According to such a theory, social control tends to vary directly, and individual freedom inversely, with the weight of the pressure to which a group is subjected from the outside, from the inside, or from both sides.

Recent history is full of examples which strikingly illustrate this principle. An extreme case is Russia. Here was a country defeated in war, torn asunder by internal strife, threatened from without and maligned from within, the masses of its people suffering not only from the wounds of World War I but also from the consequences of centuries of misgovernment; its economic apparatus worn out, its social structure toppling—in short, a country facing ruin. How was the final collapse averted? By practically abolishing individual freedom and delegating to the group, as represented by a handful of ambitious, energetic, and, above all, fanatic, commissars, complete authority over the direction and management of the economic, social, and even the spiritual life of Russia. Resource appraisal was almost totally socialized.

Although proceeding from totally different premises, fascism, like communism, is a form of government which enlarges the authority of the group at the expense of the individual. The drift toward socialism in Britain which followed the gradual and partial disintegration of the Empire and the almost catastrophic deterioration of the economic position of the ancient island workshop may be another case in point.

The motivating force behind the Marshall Plan and the European Recovery Program was the desire to prevent the advent of communist dictatorship by bettering the economic lot of the people of western Europe and thus preventing pressure from reaching the dictator-creating point. In a sense, the European Economic Com-

---

[4] Quoted by G. von Schmoller, "The Origin and Nature of German Institutions," chap. 6 of *Modern Germany in Relation to the Great War*, by various German writers, translated by William Wallace Whitelock, Mitchell Kennerley, New York, 1916.

munity and the European Free Trade Association are further efforts toward the creation of economic security and, ultimately, political security.

In contrast to these items of positive evidence of the plausibility of the pressure theory, the United States continues to shine as the great negative example. For many reasons this nation is the most prosperous, the most powerful, perhaps the happiest, certainly the luckiest country in the world. It is little wonder that the gauge registers low pressure—in general, local areas and sporadic episodes excepted—and that the individual in the United States continues to enjoy far more freedom than do people in less fortunate lands.

The Time Factor

The conflict between social and private interests develops from a fundamental difference in the nature of the group and of the individual. The group represents a succession of generations, and therefore its life must be longer than that of the individual. While history is replete with the tragic stories of the downfall of past civilizations and of glorious empires vanished from the earth, and thus furnishes proof that even groups are not permanent, yet each group, oblivious to the lessons of history, dreams of eternal life or believes that its own civilization is built upon a firmer foundation than any that has gone before. Whether, under present conditions, this trust in permanency is justified does not concern us here. What counts is the fact that the life span of the group is longer than that of the individual. If it is not permanency that the group can hope for, it certainly is a goodly share of longevity.

What has this difference in the life span of the group and of the individual to do with resource appraisal? To the average individual, the oil resources of the year 2000 may be of little concern; their size and accessibility do not interest him, for his imagination cannot follow his children and his children's children far enough into the future. The rugged individualist is not likely to be interested in the conservation of natural funds or stocks. Moreover, to the average man the reasons for the downfall of Rome are matters of indifference. His reaction is apt to be, "Well, did the ruins fall on me?" More likely than not, they did, but he is not aware of it. On the other hand, the statesman, the leader, and the thoughtful citizen who is aware of his responsibilities for the continuity of group life feel very differently.

As a result of such conflicting attitudes, social and private interests cannot agree on the "tempo" of resource development. He who regards the interest of future generations, who interprets human progress in the light of broad historical developments, is not as easily drawn into the whirlpool of profit-chasing or the excitement of the market place as is the man who lives from hand to mouth, knows no other happiness than immediate enjoyment, and whose motto is, "After us, the deluge." *The social view stresses the long-run aspects of resource appraisal; the individual is interested in immediate results. His is the short-run view.*

The "Tempo" of Exploitation

This point may be made clearer by a concrete example. A tract of timber is to be cut. The owner of the nearby paper mill is willing to pay the market price for the timber. If he can get it below the market price, so much the better. This is the extent of his interest. How cutting that timber without providing for its replacement through reforestation will affect the timber situation five or ten or twenty years hence is "none of his business." The government, on the other hand, is vitally concerned with questions of conservation, flood control, etc., and is trying to educate the wood-using public not to treat the forest as a mine but to view timber as a crop.

This example brings out the question of "tempo," to which reference was made above. The strictly private viewpoint appraises tempo purely as to its immediate effects upon the current market situation. The social viewpoint, on the other hand, weighs the effects of the rate of the exploitation of resources upon market conditions, not only of today, but also as they will probably develop in the future. Moreover, the group is concerned with aspects of the production process which lie outside the field of profit economy. Since the tempo of exploitation is a much more vital consideration in the case of the limited nonrenewable resources than in that of unlimited or of self-renewable resources, we can readily understand the keen interest which the state, as the political embodiment of the group will, takes in the conservation of the limited nonrenewable resources.

The difference in the resource interests of group and individual is largely explained by the functional division of labor between them and especially by the difference in attitudes just discussed. But the division goes even deeper, for it pertains to the division of the income derived from the utilization of resources. The selfish interest of the individual naturally strives for the maximum return, "the maximization of profit." The state, on the other hand, for the sake of harmony among classes and in order to safeguard its own permanency, may be concerned with a more equitable distribution of income than the untrammeled operation of "natural economic forces" would bring about. We cannot here follow up this line of thought, for it would lead us into the larger problems of social reform—in fact, into the social problems of our times and away from the more immediate problems of resource appraisal. But to complete this analysis we must add that within the same group the divisions between private and social interest and, with it, resource appraisal, vary from time to time. In times of danger—war, civil strife—the social or long-run aspects are stressed, but in times of peace and plenty the reins with which the group holds the individual in check are slackened.

Other Conflicts

The process of appraisal which, as we have seen, is largely dominated by the conflict between group and individual interests, has lost much of its original straight-line simplicity. Even larger and more complex social structures have resulted in a maze of conflicting interests which call for a constant balancing of pros and cons, for constant compromise. Village and town economies have merged into national economies and these, in turn, have become subject to world economic influences. Thus the areal basis of resource appraisal has continuously expanded. But the straight-line simplicity of appraisal has suffered for other reasons as well. Among these, the development of economic organization and economic processes, and the technique made possible by larger and better social organizations and by inventions and discoveries in every field of science, rank foremost in importance. This is not the place to trace this development to its origin and follow it through in all its ramifications and refinements. Three closely interrelated phases, however, deserve special mention because of their revolutionary effect on resource appraisal.

The Division of Labor.   Prior to the division of labor, man appraised his environment on the basis of its capacity to furnish him directly what he wanted. But after the division of labor separates a group into farmers and craftsmen, the directness of appraisal is partly lost. These functional divisions among individuals belonging to the same community develop into a division of labor among communities; this in time becomes interregional and international. States and nations specialize along agricultural, mining, or manufacturing lines; cities specialize in certain products. Thus wide areas lose their self-sufficiency and become dependent on interregional or international trade for the satisfaction of their wants and the attainment of their objectives. Great Britain, for instance, gets much of its food from abroad, exchanging manufactured goods or services for it. The appraisal of the English natural and cultural landscape, therefore, no longer proceeds along the straight line: How much food can the soil yield? It follows a devious line, and the query now is: How much surplus manufacture can be produced which can be exchanged for the food surpluses of others? The appraisal of the food-exporting country is inversely affected.

Modern transportation, communication, and trading and financing techniques render feasible interregional exchange on a world-wide scale. The people of central England, for numerous reasons, are exceptionally successful in the production of cutlery; they may exchange cutlery for Australian mutton and Argentine wheat. Therefore, to obtain food, they must make something totally different from food, something seemingly unrelated; if they cannot make something to exchange for food, they face starvation. Exchange thus has raised many goods to the level of "constructive" necessities. This applies not only to those goods which are used in the production and transportation of food and other necessities, but also to those which are exchanged for necessities. Thus, a Sheffielder may well view his forges and furnaces as his food resources. In a money economy, any commodity whose production enables men to earn the wages with which to buy the necessities of life is itself a necessity. The ship that carries food from surplus areas to deficiency areas is as necessary as the wheat field itself. Steel and coal, petroleum and water power, railroads and banks—in short, anything that keeps the wheels of modern world economy going—are necessities.

The Rise of Capitalism.   An essential feature of capitalistic production is the use of machines. To a large degree, it may be said that productive efficiency depends on the number and quality of machines that can be used. Hence the appraisal of the environment now stresses its capacity to yield machine and energy materials. Capitalistic production is on the whole a more efficient, but a more roundabout or indirect, way of want satisfaction. If modern man wants bread, he first digs coal and ore, makes iron and steel, builds a factory which makes agricultural implements, builds railroads that carry implements one way and farm products the other; he builds flour mills and bakeries; he establishes banks that finance, and trade that ties all these into an organic system of social economy. Even primitive man needed a stick to scratch the ground; but getting the stick was a mere incident in the task of getting the grain. Nowadays "getting the stick," which means making and operating capital equipment, assumes such importance that at times we wonder whether we are really more interested in getting bread and other consumables than in making imposing and intricate things which will help us indirectly in getting what we want. Resource appraisal today must follow this roundabout way of production.

The Introduction of Money. The most decided break in the straight line of primitive direct appraisal resulted from the introduction of money; for money, as the medium of exchange, greatly facilitates and stimulates the division of labor and, as the measure of value, makes the rise of capitalism not only easier but in many cases possible. Money has such a revolutionary effect on resource appraisal because in the minds of many it discredits abundance and puts scarcity on the throne instead. Money turns subsistence economy into profit economy, use economy into exchange[5] economy. The man who grows his own food, keeps sheep to supply wool, builds his own house from timber cut on his own land—in short, lives in a self-sufficient closed economy—produces not for a market but for his own use. The more he produces, the more he can consume. Hence he prays for rain and sunshine, each at its proper time. He is happy when crop yields are heavy, when herds and flocks increase rapidly. His hope lies in bounty, his happiness in abundance. His is a simple straight-line appraisal of values.

Not so under a money economy. Normally, the money value or price of a product falls as a result of abundance and rises as a result

[5] Barter is exchange without the use of money; its possibilities are limited.

of scarcity. (Both abundance and scarcity are understood as relatives, usually of demand.) The farmer who raises a crop for the market—a money crop, in other words, as distinguished from a supply crop—prays not for plenty but for scarcity; that is, he hopes for a small supply in his market of the commodity he wishes to sell. Needless to say, he wishes his own share of that supply to be generous, and he wants to see the commodity he sells in strong demand.

Thus in an exchange economy—also known as a market or price economy—we find a strange warping of appraisal. But we find more, namely, a conflict of interest between buyer and seller. The buyer craves abundance, the seller scarcity. Moreover, a conflict of interests develops among the sellers of the same commodity (or of commodities serving like or similar purposes) in the market. Each one would like to sell much at a higher price. The price, however, cannot be high if all sell much. Therefore each seller would like to see the others crippled in their efforts by hailstorms, insect pests, and similar destructive agents, if they are farmers, or by strikes and fires, if they are manufacturers.

One wonders why intelligent civilized man suffers such a condition, why he allows money thus to warp appraisal and destroy harmony. The explanation is found in the almost incredible stimulus to productive efficiency furnished by the division of labor, capitalistic production technique, and the use of money (or credit). For these man is willing to pay the price in terms of conflicting interest and warped appraisal because he finds it cheap in the light of the results achieved.

We have seen that human wants and social objectives, the forces behind all productive effort, have developed into a veritable maze in the course of history, as the result of the conflict of interests between individuals and social groups, between buyers and sellers, and producers and users. We have seen how the concept of necessities has changed. We have seen further that the division of labor and the capitalistic method of production have destroyed the simple straight-line appraisal of the environment as to its usefulness. Ten thousand years of civilization have completely changed resource appraisal. All values have become new.

Merely to realize that modern resource appraisal is different from the old, that it is complex and distorted, does not suffice. That realization alone does not solve our problems; but it is the first step to the solution, and it should prove an aid in grappling with the resource problems as they will be developed in the chapters that follow.

BIBLIOGRAPHY

Bauer, P. T., *Economic Analysis and Policy in Underdeveloped Countries,* Durham, N.C.: Duke University Press, 1957.

Ciriacy-Wantrup, S. V., *Resource Conservation, Economics and Policies,* Berkeley: University of California Press, 1952.

Clark, Colin, *The Conditions of Economic Progress,* London: The Macmillan Company, 1951.

Clawson, Marion (Ed.), *Natural Resources and International Development,* Baltimore: The Johns Hopkins Press (for Resources for the Future), 1964.

Galbraith, John K., *The Affluent Society,* Boston: Houghton Mifflin Company, 1958.

Galbraith, John K., "The Poverty of Nations," *The Atlantic,* October 1962.

Hansen, Alvin H., *Economic Issues of the 1960's,* New York: The McGraw-Hill Book Company, Inc., 1960.

Heilbroner, Robert L., *The Making of Economic Society,* Englewood Cliffs, N.J.: Prentice-Hall, Inc., 1962.

Heilbroner, Robert L. and Peter L. Bernstein, *A Primer on Government Spending,* New York: Vintage Books, 1963.

Hirschman, Albert C., *The Strategy of Economic Development,* New Haven: Yale University Press, 1958.

Johnson, John J. (Ed.), *The Role of the Military in Underdeveloped Countries,* Princeton, N.J.: Princeton University Press, 1962.

Kindleberger, Charles P., *Economic Development,* New York: The McGraw-Hill Book Company, Inc., 1958.

Lauterbach, Albert, *Man, Motives, and Money,* Ithaca, N.Y.: Cornell University Press, 1954.

Morris, James, *The Road to Huddersfield: A Journey to Five Continents,* New York: Pantheon Books, 1963.

Packard, Vance, *The Status Seekers,* New York: David McKay Company, Inc., 1959.

Packard, Vance, *The Waste Makers,* New York: David McKay Company, Inc., 1960.

Ward, Barbara, "We May Be Rich But They Are Happy," *The New York Times Magazine,* May 5, 1963.

3 RESOURCE APPRAISAL: TECHNOLOGICAL AND SOCIETAL ARTS

One of the chief distinctions between man and beast is man's ability consciously and consistently to change his environment. He alone can create cultural environments expansible and changeable almost at will. The beaver can build a dam, the bird a nest. But neither beaver nor bird can critically appraise its own work and systematically undertake the task of improving either the dam or the nest or the technique of dam construction or of nest building. Each normal beaver in the course of its life can rise to the same height of perfection as countless others before it, but not one inch higher. No animal is capable of enlarging the opportunities offered by its natural environment beyond the limits set by its own organism and by the unalterable genus technique at its disposal. As a result of passive adaptation to the environment, the animal organism may change. Man alone is capable of constructive criticism of his own performance and of conscious and purposeful improvement.

As was stated before, man's ability to create cultural environments is based first of all on his superior natural endowment, his native brain power, his exceptional vocal organs, his tool-making and tool-using hand, and, second, on the accumulated effects of past cultural performance. Culture is a cumulative process; it gains momentum as it proceeds.

ARTS AND CAPITAL EQUIPMENT; TECHNOLOGICAL AND INSTITUTIONAL ARTS

Functionally, cultural improvements may be divided into two groups: tangible changes of the natural environment such as canals, railroads, powerhouses, machines, churches, etc., which may be called capital equipment; and intangible cultural changes such as techniques, knowledge, acquired skill, etc. Since the arts are the driving force and the capital equipment the fixed result, attention in this chapter is focused on the arts rather than on the equipment. Arts generally function through equipment—mechanical skill through tools, religion through churches, government through executive, deliberative, and judiciary organization. Resource appraisal, besides being affected by changing wants and social objectives, ultimately depends on the state of the arts rather than on the supply of equipment.

Two categories of the arts may be distinguished: material or technical arts, that is, abilities to utilize substances and energies, on the one hand; and societal[1] or institutional arts, that is, abilities to regulate and improve human relations, on the other. Railroads, automobiles, telephones, telegraphs, and radios are means of conquering distance. Agricultural implements may be used to raise the productivity of the soil. The arts supporting and promoting material culture are material or technical arts. Apart from the arts which regulate the relationship of man to nonhuman nature, there are arts which regulate the relationship of man to man, the arts of societal cooperation, of team play, of good government. Since parliaments, churches, lodges, trade associations, and the laws regulating human relations are generally known as institutions, we may speak of the arts supporting and promoting these institutions as societal or institutional arts.

It is idle to speculate which arts came first—societal or material —and which are more important today. We know that civilization is based on the use of fire—one of the greatest triumphs in the field of material arts—on agriculture, on the domestication of animals, all of which are material arts. But it is doubtful whether these material arts could be developed without a parallel advance in the societal arts. The two groups of arts are branches of the same tree; they draw their strength from the same soil. Mutually dependent, they both contribute to the fuller growth of the tree of civilization.

Functional Classification of the Arts

Arts and their purposes are so numerous that it is difficult to

---

[1] All arts are social products, and therefore social arts in point of origin. To avoid misunderstanding, the word "societal" is chosen here in referring to this group of arts.

gain a bird's-eye view. The shortest method of presenting this multiplicity seems to be a functional classification. Functionally, arts
may be divided into two main groups: those which render more effective man's productive efforts, and those which render the environment more amenable to these efforts.[2] In both cases the end is
the same, namely, the fuller satisfaction of human wants or the more
complete attainment of social objectives.

FUNCTIONAL CLASSIFICATION OF THE ARTS

I. *Arts designed to enlarge human capacity, raise human efficiency, and
thus promote the economy of human energy.*

   A. Arts designed to improve health and to extend the duration of
   life, and thus to improve general efficiency.
      1. Preventive and curative medicine and surgery.
      2. Mental hygiene.
      3. Contraception and other methods which permit rationalized
      control of population increase. Birth control affects, generally
      favorably, the age composition of the population, and thus the
      ratio of productive to unproductive (or less productive) age
      groups.
   B. Arts designed to better the performance of the individual.
      1. Those which *directly* raise the efficiency of human activity.
         a. Education, training, etc., which improve the intellectual
         capacity, character, and spiritual qualities of men, and bring
         about a better adaptation of the worker to the work.
         b. Ways and means which improve the functioning of human
         organs and refine the perception of the senses, such as eye-
         glasses, hearing aids, radio, television, etc.
         c. Arts of using tools and simple machines which extend the
         reach and in general raise the effectiveness of the human
         body, such as hammer, pulley, etc.
         d. Arts of using devices which permit the appropriation of
         "foreign" energy, such as turbines, windmills, internal-
         combustion engines, etc.
         e. Arts of using modern complicated and automatic machines.
      2. Those which *indirectly* raise the efficiency of human activity.
         a. Methods of increasing the mobility of man (this is mainly
         accomplished with the aid of appropriated foreign energy,
         e.g., riding on horseback, riding in a train, driving an auto-

[2] In reality these two branches intertwine. Many serve both ends directly.
Others serve one but have repercussions on the other.

mobile, flying in an airplane, etc.; this is of great importance since it expands the sphere to which man can apply his activity).

    b. Ways of improving the social relations between men or groups of men by eliminating wasteful conflict.

    c. The general increase of human knowledge of facts and of laws of nature.

II. *Arts designed to render nature more amenable to human use.*

  A. Ways and means of enlarging the supply of usable matter and energy.

    1. Arts making possible the fuller exploitation of available supplies (e.g., the application of air pressure to oil wells for the purpose of recovering supplies of petroleum which cannot be produced by ordinary methods).

    2. Arts making possible the fuller utilization of products obtained (e.g., the application of the cracking process to the production of gasoline).

    3. Arts permitting the recovery of waste materials, the use of by-products and the reuse of "secondary" materials (e.g., the manufacture of celotex from cane pulp, bagasse; the manufacture of artificial leather, fabrikoid, from cottonseed; the manufacture of steel from scrap).

    4. Arts transforming substances from a less useful to a more useful form (e.g., the manufacture of rayon out of cotton linters).

  B. Arts designed to change the form of matter or energy so as to render it usable (e.g., transforming the gravitational energy of Niagara Falls into electric energy, or transforming poisonous plants into valuable food by cooking).

  C. Arts which render matter and energy mobile or increase their mobility (these are generally the same as those which make for greater mobility of man, I, B, 2, a).

This functional classification of the arts may help the reader to appreciate the diversity and multiplicity of the ways and means by which civilization is advanced. It includes both technological and institutional arts. They are the product of millenniums of patient labor, and should be viewed not as the spoils of a triumphant conqueror but as the results of a slow evolutionary process of adaptation.

INVENTIONS AS ADAPTIVE EFFORTS

The rate of progress of inventions and arts varies considerably during different periods of history. Moreover, this development follows different directions in different parts of the earth. This last-named fact is readily understood when the arts are conceived as devices or mechanisms used by various groups to adapt themselves better to their specific environment and to adapt that environment to their specific needs. The peculiar nature of a given environment and of specific needs therefore determines the general lines along which the arts develop. Besides differences in environment and needs, differences in attitudes toward material progress and the crystallization of such attitudes in patent laws and similar institutions must be taken into consideration.

Comparisons of the mechanical progress made in different countries must not ignore this causality. If they do, wrong inferences may be drawn as to the relative ingenuity or progressiveness of different peoples. Inventions have a strange appeal to mass psychology; a nation tends to identify itself with its inventors and to sun itself in their glory. Emotions and sentiments therefore play an important part, and the real nature of things is sometimes misunderstood. Referring to early American inventors, Waldemar Kaempffert, the well-known writer on science and invention, says:

> These men were as truly pioneers as if they had been Daniel Boone pushing into the wilderness with gun and axe. They were the unconscious builders of a new industrial empire, creators of a new civilization. Because of them "Yankee ingenuity" became proverbial, and Americans were regarded as the most inventive people on earth. The truth is that Americans all came from Europe and that there is nothing in the American air or drinking water that inspires a man with the idea of talking to another over a wire a thousand miles long. No matter where they may live, inventors are like painters and poets—responsive to their environment. A kind of social and economic pressure is exerted upon them, a pressure of which they are scarcely aware, a pressure that determines what they shall wear, sing, eat, think and invent.[3]

The theory that inventions are less the expressions of superior ingenuity but almost inevitable results of social conditions is supported by the fact that when a need for an invention is felt simultaneously in several places, similar inventions are the rule rather than the exception.

[3] See W. Kaempffert, "A New Patent Office for a New Age," *The New York Times Magazine*, April 10, 1932, p. 8.

American and European Inventions

Since the needs of people differ, one must expect functional variations in the general trend of inventive achievement between peoples of different nations. Different nations find themselves face to face with essentially different resource situations and problems. Their inventive efforts, therefore, must needs be directed into different channels. A comparison between this country and continental Europe brings out the importance of this diversity of inventive needs. As will be developed more fully later on, the problems which the American inventor was facing during the nineteenth century were mainly problems of labor scarcity, excess of space, and its corollary—scarcity of time. As a result, America concentrated her inventive efforts upon labor-saving devices and instruments of transportation and communication. Typical American inventions are the mechanical reaper, the sewing machine, the calculating machine, the telephone, and the air brake.

Europe, on the other hand, was never peculiarly handicapped by scarcity of labor or by excessive distances. Her troubles were of a very different nature. Crowded Europe suffered from an inadequacy of raw materials. Her effort, therefore, had to be concentrated upon exploiting to the fullest possible measure the resources which she did possess and upon finding substitutes for those which were lacking and which could not be readily obtained from the outside. Generally speaking, her effort had to be centered upon the invention of material-saving devices, as contrasted with the labor- and time-saving devices of the United States. European, especially German, progress in chemistry is readily explained in that way. Germany first made indigo from coal; being cut off from the nitrate of Chile during World War I, German chemical manufacturers made nitrogen from the air with the aid of coal and lignite. The blast furnace, the Bessemer converter, and the open hearth may be viewed as fuel-saving devices. The Martin brothers of France developed an open-hearth furnace which not only economized on fuel but also made possible the use of scrap. The Koppers by-product coke oven pointed to material savings by the scientific recovery of by-products. Such a comparison naturally stresses essential points only, and, being based on broad generalizations, it is subject to numerous exceptions. Moreover, nowadays the intercontinental exchange of scientific ideas is so well developed that differences cannot long endure and they become increasingly blurred.

Another factor which must not be lost sight of in making comparisons of the inventive achievements of different nations is the extent to which each is supported or handicapped in its effort by nature. America made marvelous progress along the lines of mechanical labor-saving devices not only because of the greater need caused by chronic labor scarcity (until recent decades), but also because no other country in the world was blessed with the same abundance of the materials from which these labor-saving devices could be made and with which they could be operated. The speed of America's progress, therefore, is partly explained by the extent and nature of her need and partly by the favorable combination of natural opportunities at her disposal. Her triumph rests on her exceptional ability to utilize her peculiar opportunities and to meet her peculiar needs.

Finally, in appraising the relationship between environment and inventiveness, the fact that environments create attitudes which in turn become cultural fixtures—established parts of the social heritage of the group—must be considered.

Historical Variations in Inventiveness

So much about the differences of place. Let us now turn to the differences of time. That in the beginning progress should be slow seems only natural. It should always be kept in mind that the first invention is infinitely more difficult than those that are based upon it. The inventions of the simple machines[4] were beyond doubt stupendous achievements of the human mind. Once in possession of this elementary knowledge, man found additional progress much easier. Moreover, for countless ages man improved his arts reluctantly, only under dire pressure. "Necessity is the mother of invention" became a commonly accepted truth. It is one of the glories of the present age that future demands are anticipated by the systematic development of the arts—which today generally means sciences—regardless of the immediate current needs. As Walter Lippmann aptly pointed out, the art of inventing has been invented and is consciously and

[4] The six so-called simple machines or mechanical powers are: lever, wedge, wheel and axle, pulley, screw, and inclined plane.

voluntarily practiced. But at first it was necessity—necessity which sprang from the pitiful contrast between man's physical abilities, on the one hand, and his ambitions and aspirations, on the other—which prompted invention. It was at that stage that the idea of the niggardliness of nature developed. To primitive man nature certainly did look niggardly. The story of the expulsion from Paradise comes to mind. "In the sweat of thy face shalt thou eat bread." While there were few people, even primitive methods applied to niggardly nature made survival possible. But, as the numbers increased, the struggle became harder; and unless methods were improved, suffering, if not destruction, followed.

At first it was despair which drove man to invent, to develop his arts. Then it was necessity. One wonders whether today, at least in those regions where occidental civilization has reached its greatest "triumphs," it is the search for more pleasure or for pleasure more fully gratified which furnishes the chief stimulus for further progress. In pecuniary society, that is, in money-using society, want gratification is generally predicated upon the possession of money. Hence, we may say that the profit motive, the acquisitive instinct of the "businessman"—in short, pleonexy, the desire to have more for its own sake—is one of the strongest impulses to improvements of the arts. However, this does not preclude the fact that many inventors invent for the thrill of inventing rather than for pecuniary gain.

Labor Supply and Mechanical Progress

Some writers have seen a close correlation between inventive progress and labor supply. Thinking more specifically of mechanical improvements, Hendrick W. Van Loon has drawn attention to this significant relationship between the scarcity or abundance of labor, especially unskilled labor, and mechanical invention. Elevating this relationship to the rank of law, some writers believe that the amount of mechanical development will always be in inverse ratio to the number of slaves that happen to be at a country's disposal. And for proof, Van Loon cites the fact that a far greater number of mechanical patents were taken out in the United States in the first sixty years of the nineteenth century by citizens of the northern states than by those of the southern. Indeed, Van Loon holds that, by and large, both the Greeks and the Romans were less inventive than the Egyptians because they relied more heavily on slave labor. This relationship between the supply of cheap unskilled labor and mechanical progress has wide popular appeal but is treated very skeptically by scientists and scholars.

The experience of the American people during the nineteenth century can hardly be considered a sufficiently broad basis on which to build a general theory. The situation was somewhat unique in two ways. In the first place, the environment offered exceptional rewards to energetic and progressive exploitation. In the second place, the population brought with them from their former homes a considerable knowledge of arts which had been developed independently under different environmental conditions. Under such circumstances, mechanical progress was facilitated both by the peculiar nature of the environment and by the previous training and experience of man. There have been, however, other periods of history in which conditions comparable to those found during our frontier days have not produced a similar progress in mechanical development. In ancient times repeatedly, the abundance of raw materials which made some kind of existence possible had reduced the pressure of population on sustenance and in that way had retarded rather than accelerated mechanical progress. Hence the human qualities must be taken into consideration. Moreover, whatever causative force is at work may produce different results in totally different physical environments.

The Recent Technical Achievement

We now turn our attention to the remarkable spurt in the development of the arts which begins slowly with the Renaissance and gains increasing momentum during the eighteenth, nineteenth, and especially the twentieth century.

Invention is not essentially different from the ordinary learning process. A widening of the opportunities to learn and a more thorough understanding of the principles of teaching should prove valuable as an indirect inducement to greater inventive activity. In addition, the cumulative nature of the inventive process must be considered. At first inventions appear as isolated achievements, but in the course of time they grow into systems of interrelated parts and interacting forces. Lewis Mumford, in his stimulating work *Technics and Civilization,* brings out this fact with striking force by introducing the concept of "the machine" as distinguished from a spattering of individual machines. "The machine," as developed by Mumford, is that maze of machine equipment which is a striking feature of modern culture in highly industrialized countries, and which has come close to holding sway over industrial peoples. This composite of machines and factories, lines of transport and communication, resembles a living organism of almost demoniac force.

Antiquity possessed great scientists, but they were too isolated in both time and space. Furthermore, human society had not yet reached those stages of stability and security which make feasible a world-wide and continued application of scientific methods and principles. In a sense, therefore, we may say that the application of science to resource utilization is a contribution of modern times. The effect of science on human productiveness is cumulative—one invention leads to another. A new discovery increases the value of an old. The inventor of today stands on the shoulders of his predecessors and they, in turn, reaped the benefits of past performances. We can push deep into the mysteries of scientific research because innumerable scientists before us have prepared the field. In the third place, the ability to accumulate larger surpluses over and above that which is necessary to sustain orderly group life and to assure normal progress deserves attention, for it is out of these surpluses that the enormous sums are taken which nowadays are spent on scientific research.

This surplus does not necessarily have to be viewed as consisting wholly of material things, for it also takes the form of leisure. We can afford to take a considerable number of our best minds out of the field of direct productive effort and divert them to the task of consciously and consistently expanding our knowledge of both abstract and applied science. Research in the field of social organization should yield similar results for our institutional development. This ability to accumulate surpluses is particularly important in view of the concentration of their control in the hands of a relatively small number of financiers who, for the time being at least, seem consciously or unconsciously to favor a more rapid development of the arts rather than a wider distribution of their products among the masses. Furthermore, it should be remembered that the rapid progress of science in our time is facilitated by the wide publicity which each discovery receives, and by the popularization through books printed in almost every language and distributed throughout the world. As a result, each new thought today stands an infinitely better chance to fall on fertile ground where, like a seed, it may sprout forth and develop into products of unexpected grandeur and epoch-making importance.

Trial and Error, Rule of Thumb, and Science

All these factors help to explain the remarkable development of the arts in modern times; but they are overshadowed by the substitution of scientific methods for the earlier methods of trial and error and rule of thumb. Primitive man was an experimenter.[5] His was the wasteful "trial-and-error" method. He tried and tried again, until by chance he hit on the right procedure and attained the desired results. To accomplish his immediate object was his sole concern. Compared with such a wasteful method, the "rule of thumb" seems quite efficient. Its superiority rests upon the utilization of past experience, of experience gained by others. A rule or even a body of rules is developed which becomes the property of priests, goldsmiths, alchemists, master artisans, guilds, etc. Oftentimes these rules are carefully guarded and handed down only by word of mouth or by practical demonstration. Thus, the apprentice and the journeyman watched the master, saw how he did his work, and carefully imitated every step and every move. After years of "learning" and practicing they "mastered" their arts.

The scientific method towers sky-high above either one of these earlier methods. Perhaps no greater revolution occurred in the relationship between man and nature—the introduction of fire not excepted—than that brought on by the introduction of science.

The word "science" comes from the Latin verb *scire*, to know. Its essence is to know why one event follows another, and to understand causal relationships. Mere sequence is turned into cause and effect. As was pointed out above, the rule-of-thumb method is marked by the blind imitation of actions which experience has proved to bring about certain desired results. Neither the teacher nor the pupil knows the reason why. They know the sequence of events but not the causal relationship. The little Indian boy who fishes with bow and arrow may have learned from his father always

---

[5] Among primitive people, the shaman, magician, or medicine man plays an important part in the promotion of arts. His power rests on the ignorance of the group and on their belief in supernatural powers.

to aim below the object, and he then knows that unless he follows this rule of thumb he cannot shoot the fish. But he does not know anything about the physical laws of the deflection of light rays which causes him to see the fish at a different place from where it actually is. He does not know that a light ray follows a different course through air and water than does an arrow propelled by a bowstring.

This personal human aspect of the rule-of-thumb method is of far-reaching significance. The Indian boy must actually watch his father; the apprentice and journeyman must be personally around the master. In the first place, this personal element renders precarious the stock of human knowledge—if indeed we may call knowledge the mastery of a few skills and the learning by heart of rules of action which are mastered without being understood. Time and time again in history it has happened that valuable arts were lost through the death of a single person. Epidemics sweeping over localities which specialized in particular branches of production repeatedly resulted in a similar loss of arts. In the second place, the personal element limits the dissemination and distribution, at least of the more complicated arts, to relatively few people. Each master could not and would not teach more than a very limited number of apprentices. A further result of this limitation of numbers was the slow progress which the arts made throughout the major portion of human history.

Depersonalization

While the arts thus based on rule of thumb are inseparable from the personality of man, science is depersonalized, in the sense that it is detached from the frailty of a single human being. It is deposited in books; it is described in mathematical and chemical formulas. These, in turn, are disassociated from the personal carriers of the arts. The introduction of science, in other words, means above all the depersonalization of that upon which human progress rests. The highest expression of science is the mathematical formula. Especially when deposited in written or printed forms, the tenets of science, the facts and relationships discovered and expressed in mathematical formulas become the almost universal and indestructible property of mankind. The Archimedean principle and the theorem of Pythagoras survived centuries of darkness during which the valuable arts of making glass, cement, alloys, and so on, were lost, to be recovered only through reinvention. Moreover, the rule of thumb can be applied only to a specific task at hand—shaping a spearhead, catching a fish, etc., while a scientific principle is applicable to innumerable specific problems calling for similar solutions.

THE LOPSIDED DEVELOPMENT OF THE ARTS

As we have seen, the superiority of the scientific method manifests itself in a tremendous acceleration of the rate of progress of the arts. Unfortunately, however, this acceleration pertains mainly or almost exclusively to the material or technological arts, and to a far lesser extent, if at all, to the societal or institutional arts. The scientific method requires proof by verification. Verification is not necessarily easy, but it is certainly possible in most technical problems. Not so in the field of societal arts. A chemist can prove his reaction, but nobody can prove that Christianity is better than Mohammedanism or that the democratic form of government is absolutely superior to monarchy, oligarchy, or dictatorship. The result is a relative institutional stagnation in the face of technological progress—*the institutional "lag."*

It would be going too far to deny all progress in the field of the societal arts. It is difficult to generalize about these manifold forms. But here, as in the field of the material arts, it holds true that wherever verification or reliable testing methods can be applied, healthy growth and real vitality are the rule. This holds true particularly in the realm of economic institutions. The corporation in its modern form and application is hardly more than one hundred years old; but in that time it has developed into one of the most progressive and virulent aspects of our social organization. The advantages of incorporation can be demonstrated, and its superiority over other forms of economic organizations as a mechanism of profit making can be verified. Even the qualifications of specific forms for specific purposes can be rendered evident.

This cannot be said of political organizations or of religious thought. Verification in the realms of politics and religion is difficult, if not impossible. Generally speaking, Republicans and Democrats are born; a Cardinal Newman who rationally selects his religion is so rare as to achieve world renown. Thus within the institutional field itself we discern striking contrasts of development. The lop-sidedness of our development has become a favorite theme. William Fielding Ogburn in his work *Social Change* fully developed the idea of "cultural lag." John Dewey noted that we rationalize freely about the atom, the spectrum, and other phases of the material arts, but when it comes to the societal arts, prejudices and traditions rule all too often. The result is that, in spite of all the technical triumphs of the western world, it is doubtful whether the common man is happier now than in the past. We have as yet failed to correlate societal and material, institutional and technological, arts. As a result, we shudder at times when we think of the powers we have called forth from the depths of the earth and out of the mysteries of creation. We feel like a baby sitting on a powder barrel playing with matches. We wonder whether the proud edifice of our industrial civilization is not going to topple down on us. Some fear that the discovery of atomic energy, perhaps man's greatest triumph, may yet prove his undoing. Some clamor for birth control for machines. But John Dewey did not blame the machine. He put the blame for present troubles on the futile effort to apply eighteenth-century principles of pecuniary society to a twentieth-century machine civilization. He said:

> What stands in the way is not a machine age, but the survival of a pecuniary age. The worker is tied helplessly to the machine, and our institutions and customs are invaded and eroded by the machine, only because the machine is harnessed to the dollar. We cling to old creeds, and we profess ideas and sentiments that have no real hold on our living activities, because a regime of pecuniary profit and loss still commands our allegiance. In this fact the contradictions of Middletown, that is, of Anytown, come to an unity. The cults and rites, the folkways and folklore of a money culture form the pattern of our life, and in them alone our industrial practices and our sentimental ideals and theories harmoniously agree. Not till we have questioned the worth of a dominantly money-civilization shall we have a religion that is more than sentimental and verbal, and achieve an integrated life.[6]

Thus Dewey pointed not only to our strength—our technical progress—but also to our weakness—our institutional backwardness.

[6] John Dewey, "The House Divided Against Itself" (review of *Middletown*), *New Republic,* April 24, 1929; reprinted by permission of the author and the *New Republic.*

What holds true of America applies with similar force to the entire western civilization. The removal of this dissonance from our life is the burning problem of the day. What resources the future holds in store depends largely on its solution.

BIBLIOGRAPHY

Buckingham, Walter, *Automation,* New York: Harper & Row, Publishers, Inc., 1961.

Finch, James K., *Engineering and Western Civilization,* New York: The McGraw-Hill Book Company, Inc., 1951.

Garrett, Alfred B., *The Flash of Genius,* Princeton, N.J.: D. Van Nostrand Company, Inc., 1963.

Jarrett, Henry (Ed.), *Science and Resources, Prospects and Implications of Technological Advance,* Baltimore: The Johns Hopkins Press (for Resources for the Future), 1959.

Kerr, Clark, John T. Dunlop, Frederick H. Harbison, and Charles A. Myers, *Industrialism and Industrial Man,* Cambridge: Harvard University Press, 1960.

Meier, Richard L., *Science and Economic Development: New Patterns of Living,* New York: John Wiley & Sons, Inc., and the Technology Press of the Massachusetts Institute of Technology, 1956.

Mumford, Lewis, *Art and Technics,* New York: Columbia University Press, 1952.

Singer, Charles J. and others (Eds.), *History of Technology,* New York: Oxford University Press, 1956.

Spicer, Edward H. (Ed.), *Human Problems in Technological Change,* New York: Russell Sage Foundation, 1952.

Usher, Abbott P., *A History of Mechanical Inventions,* Cambridge: Harvard University Press, 1954.

Ward, Barbara, *Five Ideas That Change the World,* New York: W. W. Norton and Company, 1959.

4 THE NATURE AND SOURCES OF ENERGY

THE NATURE OF ENERGY

Energy and Matter

Modern science has broken down the barriers that long separated energy and matter as two distinct things. Scientists now view matter as a manifestation of energy, know the formula for the conversion of energy into matter and of matter into energy, and have learned how to convert certain fissionable elements of matter into atomic or nuclear energy.

Although aware of this scientific interpretation of the nature of energy and matter, the workaday world continues to think and speak of energy and matter as distinct and separate categories. One may realize that coal is energy but still differentiate between the substance coal which is mined, hauled, and burned, and the energy which is released when coal is burned. One may be aware that water is energy but still differentiate between the substance which quenches his thirst and the electricity which Niagara Falls generates. Food provides us with both energy, in the form of heat or the capacity to do work, and substance, which maintains our body.

Animate and Inanimate Energy

The examples just cited illustrate a highly significant division of energy forms into *animate,* i.e., those functioning through living organisms (plants, animals, bacteria, molds, fungi, etc.), and *inanimate,* i.e., those derived from nonliving matter, especially the fossil fuels, coal, oil, and gas, and from falling water. Animate energy, in turn, is divided into biotic and muscular energy. Muscular energy is the energy applied by an animal to useful work such as pulling a cart or lifting a weight. Biotic energy is that associated with the processes of life and growth. To be able to do work an

62

animal must live, and to live it must eat. The bulk of the food or feed intake is needed to provide biotic energy; only a fraction can be spared for muscular energy. This dependence of muscular energy on life is vital to its proper appraisal. It accounts for much of the inferiority of animate energy compared with inanimate energy.[1]

Biotic energy generated in plants is one of the main sources of useful objects obtained by man, especially by preindustrial man. Without it neither food nor feed can be produced. Timber and many other forms of vegetation serve useful purposes in providing shelter, utensils, tools, etc. Agrarian people rely almost exclusively on animate energy in both its forms—muscular and biotic. Of the two, the biotic may well be the more important.

Other Kinds of Energy

Energy, often defined as the capacity to do work, has many meanings and diverse manifestations. For one thing, work itself can mean any manifestation of energy in space and time, or it can refer to useful work, i.e., work useful to man, directed toward some human objective. When the potential energy of snow at a high altitude is released as an avalanche, a colossal amount of work is being done, but it is not useful and it may be highly destructive. In this study of resources, interest naturally centers in useful work, although the importance of the destructive work of the forces of nature is fully recognized as "resistances." One speaks of mechanical energy such as that of the drop hammer, of chemical energy released when coal is burned or in the form of active acids, of electrical energy manifesting itself as heat, power, or light, and so forth. Chemical energy locked in coal is available energy; when the coal has been burned the energy may have been spent in doing work or it may have been diffused as radiation energy.

When we speak of different kinds of energy, such as potential, kinetic, animate, inanimate, available, diffused, electrical, or chemical, we should be aware of the inaccuracy of our terminology. It should be clear from the aforesaid that energy, like time and space, is a characterless concept—there can be no good or bad energy. To be exact, therefore, we should speak of different manifestations of energy. The energy of a coolie naturally reveals itself in a different manner from that contained in gasoline or in coal. Different forms

[1] For a fuller development of this comparison, see chap. 5.

of energy require different channels for their conversion into work. Thus, sunshine is converted by chlorophyll into starch or sugar or protein, whereas the energy contained in steam may call for a reciprocating engine or turbine. Energy in food or feed can be converted into work by means of organisms, but dynamite and TNT are harnessed by means of mechanisms.

Elementary and Derived Energy

The sunshine which the green leaf through photosynthesis makes available to the growing plant as carbon and carbon compounds is clearly elementary energy. Whether the vital energy possessed by living organisms and gravitational energy are likewise elementary seems less certain. The chemical energy stored up in the sugar or starch of living plants and the carbon of coal, petroleum, etc., is derived energy. All animate or muscular energy is derived energy, dependent on food intake.

Elementary energy furnishes the starting point of a long row of derivatives which modern production processes tend to lengthen. Primitive man drew energy either directly from the sun, or indirectly, through the plant or animal as food. The modern process of energy utilization is generally more roundabout. We tap the chemical energy of coal and turn it into heat; the heat, applied to water, raises steam, a kind of mechanical energy valued for its expansive power and which can be given direction and controlled in a steam engine. The resulting mechanical energy appears as rotation and, with the aid of a dynamo, may be converted into electrical energy. This in turn may be translated into heat, light, or chemical or magnetic or mechanical energy, as the case may be.

Functional Appraisal of Kinds of Energy

The reason for this evident tendency toward an increasing complexity of energy economy lies in the functional differences of various energy forms. The ideal energy for locomotion is different from the ideal energy required for stationary work. Thus gasoline, a highly compact energy carrier which furnishes much energy per unit of weight and volume, is more suitable for driving an automobile than is wood or peat. To certain tasks either mechanical or chemical energy can be applied. Thus, wood can be turned into wood pulp by means of either chemical energy or mechanical energy, although the so-called chemical and mechanical wood pulps do not always serve the same purpose.

Electrical energy owes much of its popularity to its versatility. As was mentioned before, it can be converted into heat, light, or chemical, magnetic, and mechanical energy. From the economic point of view, it can do practically anything. However, its great defect is the cost of its storage. Chemical energy on the whole is more storable, and many carriers of chemical energy likewise excel electricity in transportability. But improvement in the technique of power transmission might enhance the popularity of electricity, especially of hydroelectricity. For electricity generated from coal and oil stands to profit most from improvements in the conversion of heat into electricity. If it takes half as much coal to generate a kilowatt-hour, the effect is the same as if the transportability of coal had been increased by 100 percent. Here we can only touch on the general question of the relative desirability of different forms of energy.

Availability of Energy and the Laws of Thermodynamics

It has long been a fundamental tenet of physics that the total supply of matter and energy in the universe is constant. To the physicist the law of the conservation of matter and energy is basic. The economist, however, is less interested in the totality of the supply than in its availability. Unfortunately, the law of the conservation of energy, generally referred to as the first law of thermodynamics, furnishes man no guarantee of an undiminishing supply of *available* energy. For the second law of thermodynamics, equal in importance to the first, reveals the fact that the "quality" of energy tends to deteriorate, if we may use that expression for a characterless abstraction, and therefore the available supply tends to decrease. This deterioration in general manifests itself in the increase of the wave length of the energy stream. Energy can become so "diffuse" that it ceases to be available.

Human Energy

There remains to be discussed one more category of energy, human energy. Just as man plays a unique role in the overall scheme of resource development, he also occupies a unique place in the realm of energy. In fact it is the uniqueness of human energy that accounts for the uniqueness of man's role in the resource scheme.

As a source of physical energy, as a power unit used for physical work, man is hopelessly outclassed by animals and even more by the power-driven machine. A ton of coal with the aid of the proper appliances can produce more mechanical work than can a thousand men in the same period of time. Moreover, the thousand men have to eat. Under ordinary circumstances their food would cost a multiple of the cost of the coal and of the overhead that could be charged to the work to be performed.

But not all the coal in the world can contribute as much mental and spiritual guidance, as much planning, inventing, and aspiring as one man. Man's forte is brain, not brawn. In the application of brain power man towers high above all other creatures. In the great plan of creation he seems to have been selected to be the planner of schemes and events, the director, coordinator, and manager of forces aimed at a given end, the thinker, the inventor, the discoverer, the dreamer, and, above all, the aspirer.

There is no substitute for these higher forms of human energy. The full recognition and appreciation of this uniqueness and indispensability of human energy are the key to all energy economy and resource strategy. The highest aim of that strategy must be to release man from physical toil as much as possible without impairing his physical fitness. Only in that way can specialization be brought to its fullest fruition. Using man as a beast of burden or a work animal is a flagrant violation of the principle of specialization. Civilizations will flourish or perish according to the extent to which they follow this simple rule. Therein lies the real blessing inanimate energy holds out to man. The greatest defect of ancient civilizations which were based chiefly on animate energy is that they thwarted man's higher abilities and aspirations; vice versa, the greatest source of strength of the modern resource pattern is that it enables him to play the part for which his superior mental endowment has prepared him.

Past civilizations, such as the Athenian under Pericles, achieved for a small group at the expense of a submerged majority what the modern resource pattern—theoretically, at least—makes possible for all. Under the ancient resource pattern, specialization meant a functional division between a ruling minority and the mass of ruled, partly enslaved people. The modern resource pattern makes possible a division between man—the inventor, planner, director, and aspirer—and the inanimate forces of nature. Few will deny that the latter system has inherent advantages over the former. Unfortunately, however, there is a wide gap between what is possible under the modern resource pattern and what is actually being achieved. It is to be hoped that this gap will grow narrower in time.

History teaches that man is apt to apply his unique energies best in an atmosphere of freedom. Thus the problem of energy strategy merges with that of good government and the development of the societal arts. Institutions have as much to do with the ultimate efficacy of energy use as have engines, machines, and logarithm tables.

SOURCES OF ENERGY

Atomic Nature of Energy

Eugene E. Ayres described the atomic nature of energy in the following words:

> All of the energy which the skill and ingenuity of man has contrived to convert to useful work is of atomic origin, and it seems that nearly all of the work of the future will come in various ways from this ultimate source. Our converted energy now comes from the sun, where the transmutation of hydrogen to helium is believed to provide energy in the form of light with minor supplements of thermal and ultraviolet radiation. This accounts for all of our power except for the relatively tiny additional amounts that come from radioactive transformations in the earth itself.

> The present convenient and economic sources of energy are petroleum, natural gas, and coal—which are often called "stored sunlight" because they were formed from carbon dioxide and water in living organisms by the influence of solar radiation—and hydro-electric power which comes from the precipitation on our land areas of the water evaporated by sunlight from our hydrosphere. Sources of energy less convenient or uneconomic are: vegetation which can be burned to produce about as much energy as the amount of solar energy absorbed in its growth, or which can be converted to such liquid fuels as gasoline or alcohol with a considerable loss of energy; wind, which is an erratic consequence of solar radiation; and the direct conversion of sunlight into forms of energy which can be

controlled, intensified, or stored. There is no doubt that some of these secondary sources of solar energy will become exceedingly important in the rather near future.

The heat of the earth itself is believed to come from the atomic degradation of a few of our elements. A little of this heat is being utilized now for power generation. And our atomic scientists . . . separate these radioactive elements from the inert materials with which they are associated in the earth in order that the effects of atomic degradation may be concentrated and controlled. These earthly sources of atomic energy may become important in the more distant future by virtue of nuclear and engineering research.

The only source of energy which may not be atomic in origin is that derivable from the kinetic energy of the earth's rotation. A little of this appears in the tides of our oceans, and a very little can be, and ultimately will be, harnessed.[2]

Solar Origin of Energy

Fig. 3[3] shows the various ways in which the earth receives solar energy, and the main manifestations of this energy on this planet.

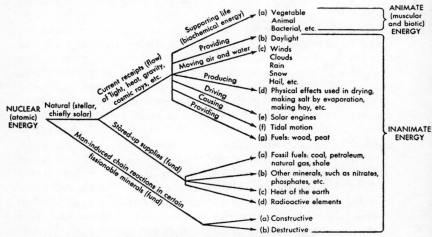

FIGURE 3. Energies—Their Origin and Manifestations

[2] Eugene E. Ayres, "Major Sources of Energy," a paper read during the 28th annual meeting of the American Petroleum Institute, November 9, 1948, p. 109.

[3] This diagram is adapted from one in S. S. Wyer, *Man's Shift from Muscle to Mechanical Power*, pamphlet prepared for the Fuel-Power and Transportation Educational Foundation, Columbus, Ohio, p. 2.

The dichotomy of current receipts (flow) and stored-up supplies (fund) of solar radiation in this figure is of particular significance. Its importance will be developed as the analysis of energy proceeds. The dichotomy of animate and inanimate energy already mentioned will also be further discussed below.

Energy Sources Classified

With special emphasis on the manner of present and future utilization, energy sources may be classified as follows:

CLASSIFICATION OF MAJOR ENERGY SOURCES[4]

I. Continuous or renewable sources of energy.
   A. Direct solar radiation utilized:
      1. Directly by means of:
         a. Optical devices such as reflectors, lenses, etc.
         b. Photochemistry, photoelectricity, and thermoelectricity.
      2. Indirectly through:
         a. Photosynthesis, upon which living organisms depend for food and feed and which in addition provides many useful materials (e.g., wood and other building materials, rubber, fibers, etc.), as well as fuels (wood, alcohol, and gasoline extracted from vegetation).[5]
         b. Use of:
            (1) Water raised by the sun, moved by the winds, and caught on the descent.
            (2) Winds.
            (3) Difference in temperature between atmosphere and:
               (a) The earth ("the heat pump").
               (b) The ocean.
   B. The heat of the earth (traced to atomic fission) tapped through volcanic vents.
   C. Tidal power.
II. Exhaustible or unrenewable sources of energy.
   A. Fissionable elements yielding atomic or nuclear energy through acceleration of fission.
   B. Fossil fuels.
      1. Coal.
      2. Oil (including oil shale and tar sands).
      3. Natural gas.

[4] Based largely on Eugene E. Ayres, *op. cit.*, pp. 110–125.
[5] Carbon dioxide present in the atmosphere and hydrosphere may yield carbon which by synthesis with hydrogen may yield hydrocarbon fuels.

Use of Energy Sources

Up to now only a small beginning has been made in the direct use of sunshine for mechanical work. In the future man will be forced to rely increasingly on this inexhaustible source of energy. Until now, the actual use of solar energy has been mainly as animate energy, both muscular and biotic, in the form of food and feed, useful animal and vegetable products, and work done by man and beast. It included the use of wood to make fire, and until the Industrial Revolution, it was by far the most important source of energy available to man.

The extraction of gasoline and alcohol from vegetation is as yet largely uneconomical but will probably play a major role in future energy utilization, as will also probably the extraction of carbon from carbon dioxide in the atmosphere and hydrosphere for use in the synthesis of hydrocarbons. Only modest beginnings have been made with the use of wind power and of temperature differences, but the use of falling water in the form of hydroelectric power has assumed considerable proportions.

By far the most important sources of energy in terms of mechanical work performed are the unrenewable fossil fuels, coal, oil, and natural gas.

Ayres has discussed the prospects of future energy sources and their uses. A report on his analysis follows.

> The possible sources of continuous energy are reviewed and most of them discarded as insignificant in potentiality. There are only a few sites where tides are high enough to yield worthwhile power. The heat of the earth's interior is available only through a few geysers and similar geologic oddities. Wind power is neither dependable nor great in potential magnitude. Engines based on the temperature difference between the ocean's surface and depths in the tropics would require a terrific investment and would be located where power is not greatly needed. No one has yet suggested a means of using the electrical potential which exists between the earth and its atmosphere. Heat pumps, by which heat is moved from the earth to a house, just as a refrigerator moves it from a closed box to the outside . . . would provide only a small amount of energy. Use of water power can be expanded perhaps eightfold, but its potential is only a minor part of our future energy needs.
>
> One of the most immediately feasible means of using the sun's

energy is through extending and improving conventional agriculture and forestry. Timber from three million square miles of forest, about the area of the United States, could supply the world's present energy requirements indefinitely. Wood is expensive to gather and handle, but it can be converted into gas, alcohol, or gasoline through techniques now known. Intensive use of the soil to supply both food and fuel does, however, pose serious problems of maintaining fertility and water supply. Mr. Ayres estimates that a century hence vegetation could supply energy equivalent to only half the world's total energy consumption at present. This represents a tenfold increase in use. Improved knowledge of the photosynthesis reaction by which plants form vegetation may release us from dependence on soil and water.

Solar heating of houses is, on the cosmic scale of this discussion, on the verge of practicality now. The principal present problem is one of reducing investment cost; further development, together with rising fuel costs, can probably solve this. Within a century, solar energy may handle half the world's space-heating load.

Use of solar energy for power is a promising possibility, and a technical problem, perhaps the most important one in providing tomorrow's energy. . . . Given plenty of cheap electric power from solar sources, gasoline could be synthesized from water and atmospheric carbon dioxide to fuel automobiles and airplanes. Despite the development required, Mr. Ayres suggests that solar energy equivalent to present total world energy consumption will be possible within a century.

Altogether, Mr. Ayres visualizes continuous sources as supplying within a century energy equivalent to twice the world's present consumption. Of this continuing energy, solar power would provide half; vegetation, a quarter; waterfalls, a seventh, and solar space heating, a tenth.

How much energy the world will use a hundred years from now is anybody's guess. In addition to the demonstrated continuing increase in consumption, 50 per cent in 50 years, coming decades will see tremendous losses from converting one form of energy to another, notably, coal to liquid fuels, and, most important, coal to electricity.

Evaluation of our present underground reserves of fossil fuels, including uranium for atomic energy, of course requires some estimate of future demand. . . . The important point is that continually rising demand will eventually reach a level completely beyond that which fossil fuels can supply. Either continuous energy sources, principally solar power, must be used, or demand growth must halt.[6]

CHIEF SOURCES OF ENERGY TODAY

At the present time there are two main sources of energy: food and feed, the sources of animate energy; and fuels, especially the fossil fuels but including wood and other vegetation, the sources of inanimate energy. In view of their dominant position in the present energy scheme, a brief examination of their nature and functions is called for.

The Chemical Wheel of Life

Food and feed constitute major products of that grandiose process of living nature, powered directly by the sun and based on photosynthesis. The energy of the sun is utilized by the chlorophyll of leafy green plants and in the plankton of salt and fresh water. The green plant and perhaps some bacteria can make use of solar radiation in the photosynthesis of such substances as sugars, starches, proteins, etc., acceptable as food or feed to animals and fungi. These substances are built up from elements present in air, water, and soil. Green plants, therefore, are the prime resources of all living substances. They are "energy parasites" on the sun; animals and fungi, in turn, are "food parasites" on green plants.[7] While animals can feed only on plants—herbivores—or on other animals—carnivores—or on both—omnivores—and can thus only indirectly tap certain energies of the sun, they can benefit directly from other solar energies, namely, light, heat, and ultraviolet rays. These direct and indirect uses of solar energy are interchangeable to a certain extent, for a warm climate and fuller exposure to ultraviolet rays reduce the food requirements; on the other hand, up to a certain limit, deficiency of warmth can be made up by increased food consumption. Needless to say, body warmth can also be obtained from fire and can be conserved by means of clothing and shelter with a similar effect on food requirements.

[6] See *Industrial Bulletin,* Arthur D. Little, Inc., Cambridge, Mass., February, 1949, p. 1.

[7] The terminology here is that used in H. G. Wells, J. S. Huxley, and G. P. Wells, *The Science of Life,* Doubleday & Company, Inc., New York, 1931, vol. 2, book 6, chap. 5.

In so far as the sun, by acting on air and water, affects climatic as well as soil conditions, the contributions made to the process of photosynthesis by these other agents are in part traceable to the sun. The functional relationship of these various factors is shown in Fig. 4.[8]

This food cycle is referred to by Huxley as the chemical wheel of life. It is not complete without the bacterial action producing decay, for decay is not only the end but also the beginning of life. Bacterial coloring matter and chlorophyll are chemically closely related, but the functions of the two seem to be reversed. Chloro-

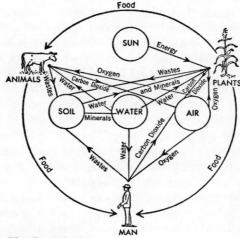

FIGURE 4. The Food Cycle in Nature

phyll synthesizes sugars, starches, etc., whereas bacterial coloring matter, associated with a different mineral, seems to possess the power to break up the product of photosynthesis. The turning of the great "chemical wheel of life" is aptly described by Huxley. It is given here in somewhat condensed form.

Most living substances consist of carbon, hydrogen, oxygen, and nitrogen. Other elements, such as sodium, potassium, calcium, iron, phosphorus, sulfur, chlorine, iodine, and perhaps silicon, copper, and zinc, are equally essential, though present only in traces.

[8] C. J. Pieper and W. L. Beauchamp, *Everyday Problems in Science*, Scott, Foresman and Company, Chicago, 1925, p. 82.

Almost all the carbon needed in life is taken from the air where it occurs as carbon dioxide in the average amount of 0.03 percent. It is also held in solution in water, though in very varying proportions. The other substances reach green plants in the form of inorganic salts dissolved in water. The hydrogen which also enters in the form of water is used together with carbon dioxide to produce sugar, a carbohydrate, oxygen being returned to the air or water. Oxygen, which is taken chiefly from the air, is needed to sustain the oxidation necessary to the life not only of green plants but of all plants and most animals. Some bacteria and fungi are able to extract oxygen from the substances on which they feed.

The green plant thus effects a synthesis of organic carbon and nitrogen compounds on which the rest of life subsists in parasitic fashion. To support animal life higher than that of some protozoa, the plant carbohydrates and plant proteins must not be of simpler chemical nature than sugars and amino acids. Once having entered into animal life, they continue to circulate in the animal kingdom until dissolution or decay sets in. Decay is the work of special bacteria, and thus forms an integral phase of the cycle of life. Different bacteria perform special functions. Through decay and oxidation, the carbon, nitrogen, and other elements of once living substances reappear with few exceptions in air and water. A variant of this general rule is brought about by the presence of fungi and molds which are parasitic on decay; they can utilize lower forms of food than animals. In either case, the carbon makes a complete circle, and the wheel of life turns from green plant to animal and on to bacteria and through them to decay and back again to the green plant. The sun furnishes the energy that turns the wheel; the green leaf is the prime mover, as it were; and animals and bacteria and other living substances function so as to preserve the equilibria without which the wheel does not turn smoothly.

Man's Part in the Process of Life

Man is caught in this eternal process. "From dust thou art, to dust thou shalt return." But man is not caught altogether helpless; for he puts his hand to the wheel and, though he cannot stop it, he can materially modify the effect of its grinding work on him. At times he overreaches himself in his attempt to improve on nature. Inadequately aware of the importance of balances and equilibria which the ecologist is gradually revealing, he succeeds in gaining a little now at the expense of greater loss later on. As yet, human institutions and social organizations have not found the proper harmony between individual needs and wants of the day, and social and world requirements measured over longer periods. But here we are not concerned with the critical aspects of man's effort to utilize the sun and to exploit the process of nature; we merely describe these efforts.

Not satisfied with such direct benefits as he derives from sunshine, man has developed numerous ways of utilizing solar radiation indirectly and of appropriating energies other than his own. This effort has taken two main lines. First of all, man forever tries to enlarge the range of his food supply. Second, he constantly seeks to appropriate energy for purposes of work. Food enables man to work. "Foreign" energy may be substituted for his own energy, or it may supplement it.

Moreover, man can appropriate the energies stored up in living plants not only through food consumption, but also by turning them into alcohol, a source of power. We may thus view plants as storage batteries of energy. Naturally they developed their capacity to store energy not to serve man, but to assure the preservation of their own kind. "The storage device is a defence mechanism made necessary by the intermittency of sunshine from day to day and from summer to summer."[9] Finally, the energy locked up in plants, especially in wood, can be released by fire.

Furthermore, man can use plants indirectly through animals which feed on them, human slavery being but a variant of this form of energy utilization. Some animals are used for work or as beasts of burden; in others, the energy stored up by the animal (in such a form as the milk provided by nature for the preservation of the species) is diverted to human use. What is more, through breeding, man can greatly enhance the capacity of animals to convert feed into energy available to him, and he can likewise speed up and otherwise aid the conversion by green plants of solar radiation into carbohydrates and other sources of energy. Thus the domestication of animals, animal husbandry, and agriculture become important aspects of human energy problems. Moreover, through the inven-

[9] H. G. Wells, J. S. Huxley, and G. P. Wells, *op. cit.*

tion of tools and machines the control over and the direction of these energies may be greatly improved.

To summarize, we can say that man, apart from drawing certain direct benefits from current supplies of sunshine, can utilize the supplies indirectly by appropriating both food and energy from both plants and animals. Moreover, he can modify the processes of nature to his own interest and thus consciously enlarge his energy supply.

Current Stellar Radiation as a Source of Inanimate Energy

We now turn to the current receipts portion of Fig. 3. The sun, together with gravity, causes movements of the air as well as of water, which man can utilize in many ways. Of the water which reaches the land in the form of rainfall, chiefly the "surface run-off," the rivers can be used for purposes of generating mechanical energy. The winds are utilized directly through windmills and sailing ships. The energy of moving, especially falling, water is utilized directly by objects floating downstream and indirectly with the aid of water wheels and water turbines. The relation of winds and rainfall to climate and, through it, to all organic life is fundamental. The heat of the sun's rays now can be applied to solar engines which turn sunshine into mechanical energy; but as yet, this method of utilization is in its infancy. Finally, the current supply of solar radiation is used as heat in salt making, hay making, the drying or dehydration of fruits and vegetables, and for similar purposes.

Inanimate Energy and Stored-up Supplies of Solar Energy

We now turn to the stored-up supplies of solar energy. Stores of solar energy, such as coal deposits and oil sands, are said to reflect defects of the chemical cycle of life. When the balance of the chemical process of life and decay is disturbed, the "wheel" cannot turn smoothly. Such disturbances cause leakages which paradoxically have now assumed transcendent importance for man. Our coal deposits, petroleum reserves, supplies of natural gas, the nitrate fields of Chile, the phosphate rock of Florida, and chalk and limestone deposits found in many parts of the world owe their existence to these imperfections in the process of life and decay. Such mineral accumulations may be viewed as the results of disturbed equilibria.

Coal fields are the result of "carbon spilling over," as it were, "shunted out of the cycle of life," "food capital locked out of circulation and hidden away for hundreds of millions of years." The explanation for such irregularities may be found in cataclysmic or evolutionary changes of the crust of the earth, which withhold the oxygen necessary to complete the decay that keeps the wheel turning. Because of the inadequacy of oxygen, the carbon does not reappear as carbon dioxide, in which form it would be available to molds and fungi. It therefore cannot be drawn back into the food cycle. Apart from such discrepancies in the cycle of life and decay, purely inorganic processes may cause digressions from the rule, of which the mineral salt deposits are a silent witness.

It is the part of our modern civilization to take advantage of these long-hidden stores of energy, and it is to their exploitation that we owe much of our material progress and speed. The exploitation of these stored supplies of solar energy is rendered fully possible only by the exploitation of other minerals, especially metals. As conditions are today, the modern large-scale coal and petroleum economy is intimately related to the iron and copper economy. The relation between the machine resources and the energy resources is very close—coal supplies the energy required to produce iron, and the iron is needed to harness the coal.

Atomic Energy

The other source of unrenewable energy, fissionable elements, is coming into wider use. Its spectacular unveiling at Hiroshima has given it world-wide advertising. Remote, indeed, must be the human habitation which the echoes of that great explosion did not reach.

There is still much that is not known, even to the initiated, about atomic energy. Little is known about the size of deposits of the fissionable elements uranium and thorium, but that they are limited and, like coal and oil, exhausted by use, is an established fact. Because of its military potentialities, research in and production of atomic energy is everywhere a function of the government, with limited and controlled participation by private enterprise. The extent to which, and the conditions under which, atomic energy will become a source of industrial power, replacing or supplementing the fossil fuels and falling water, is not yet answered. A good deal of research is now directed at finding the answers.

The application of atomic energy to the economies of the underdeveloped lands may lay the foundation for global industrialization. While there are technical difficulties, they can be overcome in time. Probably more serious are the political problems stemming from international distrust and fear of abuse.

CONVERSION OF ENERGY

The problem of energy conversion is of such importance that it deserves special mention. All energy is either turned into work or converted into another form of energy. This conversion of one form of energy into another may be either unintentional, caused by the imperfection of method and equipment, or it may be intended for a specific purpose. In the attempt to transform the energy of coal into work by turning water into steam and applying the pressure of the expanding steam to the piston of a reciprocating engine or the blades of a turbine, a considerable portion of the energy of the coal is turned into other forms of energy, especially into radiation and heat. It is thus lost; and we speak of leakage, conductive and frictional losses, and so forth. Apart from this unintentional and undesirable conversion of one form of energy into another form, a great deal of intentional conversion takes place. The demand of modern industry for specific forms of energy suitable to specific purposes and the urgent efforts of the power industry to increase its market join to render the conversion of one form of energy into another increasingly common.

MODERN ENERGY UTILIZATION

In the effort to improve the conversion factor and to adapt the energy forces to the specific requirements of modern industry, the engineer and scientist constantly develop new means of energy utilization. If crude oil burned under a boiler yields only a fraction of its energy in the form of usable energy, it is refined, perhaps subjected to processing such as cracking and hydrogenation, and thus induced to yield more energy. The same principle is applied

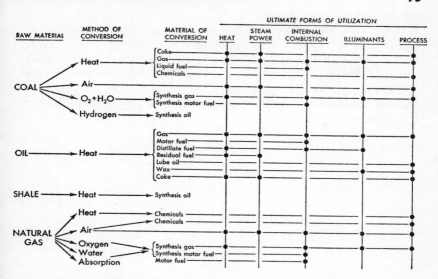

FIGURE 5. Mineral Fuels, Their Conversion and Utilization

to coal, shale, and natural gas. Fig. 5 is shown here merely to illustrate the diversity of effort.[10]

This brief outline of some of the basic facts and general principles pertaining to the physical, technical, and scientific aspects of natural energy was given not only for its own sake but especially as an introduction to the next chapter, which deals with the social and economic implications of the major changes in energy utilization, especially of the mechanical revolution which marks the shift from animate to inanimate energy.

BIBLIOGRAPHY

Ayres, Eugene and Charles A. Scarlott, *Energy Sources—The Wealth of the World,* New York: The McGraw-Hill Book Company, Inc., 1952.

Energy Resources and Government, Joint Economic Committee, United States Congress, Washington, D.C.: United States Government Printing Office, 1960.

[10] Fig. 5 is based on a diagram distributed to the Round Table Conference on "The Rôle of Chemistry in the World's Future Affairs," H. E. Howe, Chairman, Williamstown Institute of Politics, Sixth Session (1926), and redrawn by Eugene E. Ayres.

Lichtblau, John H. and Dillard P. Spriggs, *Energy Policy and Competition*, New York: Petroleum Industrial Research Foundation, 1961.

Schurr, Sam H., Bruce C. Netschert, Vera F. Eliasberg, Joseph Lerner, and Hans H. Landsberg, *Energy in the American Economy, 1850–1975*, Baltimore: The Johns Hopkins Press (for Resources for the Future), 1960.

Thirring, Hans, *Energy for Man*, Bloomington: Indiana University Press, 1958.

5 CHANGING USES OF ENERGY

THE MECHANICAL REVOLUTION

Since the appropriation of fire and the domestication of animals probably no greater single change has occurred in the availability of energy to man than the coming of steam. The mechanical revolution marks the shift from one-sided reliance on animate energy to increasing dependence on inanimate energy. This shift in the energy supply has affected the materials used by man, it has revolutionized his methods of work and forms of social and economic organization, and it has caused geographical adjustments as well as political realignments, to say nothing of its repercussions on the very thoughts and feelings of all those who have come under its spell, even on philosophy and religion.

Since, as we have seen, the resource appraisal of our environment depends on our own wants, aims, and methods, the mechanical revolution in a very real sense has remade the resource map of the world. One cannot, therefore, understand the resource setup of the modern world without a full appreciation of the mechanical revolution. This understanding, moreover, is aided by a comparison between the resource pattern of a region such as southern China, which has as yet been but little touched by the magic finger of steam and its companions, and the resource pattern of the industrialized Occident.

History and Energy

If we consider that nothing on this earth can happen without the expenditure of some energy and if we interpret the meaning of energy broadly enough, the suggestion of Fairgrieve that human history is the story of man's increasing control over energy may not seem unreasonable. Let us listen to his argument:

. . . it may be said that in its widest sense on its material side history is the story of man's increasing ability to control energy. By energy we mean the capacity for doing work, for causing—not controlling—movement, for making things go or making things stop, whether they be trains or watches or mills or men. In order that anything may be done, energy is required. Man's life is taken up by the one endeavor to get and to use as much energy as possible and to waste as little as possible. Any means whereby he can get more or waste less marks an advance, and is important in the history of the world. All the discoveries which have been made of how to do things, inventions as we call them, which have marked various stages of progress, are not merely rather interesting facts that have very little to do with history. They have everything to do with it. The inventions of hieroglyphics, of writing, of numerals, of printing, of the compass, of spades, wheels, needles, of steam-engines, and of banknotes have had enormously important effects on the course of the history of the world, and are important just in so far as they enable man to use or to save energy.[1]

Fairgrieve then goes on to explain more fully how social, military, and constitutional history—in short, all cultural history—can be interpreted as a process of improved control over energy. The machinery necessary for the use of energy consists not merely of physical equipment but includes social institutions as well. Changes of government must be interpreted as alterations and repairs of this machinery. The eneregy used to make, repair, and improve the machinery, though not directly used for the satisfaction of human wants, is not wasted; neither is the energy required to refine the lubricating oil without which the machinery does not run smoothly. Banks, organized exchanges, and newspapers furnish the lubricating oil of our economic system.

The idea that the advance of civilization is marked by an improved energy economy can well be defended. But we must be sure to recognize the economy of energy in all its forms and disguises. We meet it in the open in the form of a central power station that makes two kilowatts grow where one grew before. It is embodied in a glass which allows the free passage of the health-giving ultraviolet rays of the sun. More often its efforts are less overt. It is hidden in the mathematical formula. It makes law and order worth

[1] James Fairgrieve, *Geography and World Power,* E. P. Dutton & Co., Inc., New York, 2nd ed., 1921, p. 3.

while. It gives vitality to the peace pact which settles the disputes between nations, and lends value to the agreement which ends the strife between social groups, especially "labor and capital." It is the lifeblood of education. Thus the rationalized economy of energy is man's greatest triumph and his biggest task. The aim of that economy is a fuller life for the living multitude and enhanced security for the multitudes yet to be born.

A brief review of human history shows clearly the vital importance of changing energy supplies. It is often said that man was not man until he could use fire, a chemical energy with a thousand uses; he was not civilized until he had learned through domestication to use the "foreign" energy of animals and, through agriculture, to harness better the "free" energy of solar radiation and the chemical energies of light, water, and soil. Slavery, an institution governing the use of "foreign" animate energy, was a vital factor in history, though hardly one marking as fundamental a change as those brought on by the discovery of fire, the domestication of animals, and the introduction of agriculture. The same applies to gunpowder, another source of energy which has redrawn maps and decided the fate of nations. The wholesale supplementation of the ancient forms of energy by the modern form, inanimate energy derived from fossil fuels—in short, the mechanical revolution—means another fundamental change in man's control over energy.

One-Sided Determinism

The mechanical revolution, therefore, is here viewed as more than a mere dividing line of history. It is a Great Divide. Lest such a claim create the false impression of one-sided materialism, a word of explanation is added. It is fully realized that the importance of making available new forms or additional amounts of energy can be exaggerated; and that, correspondingly, the equal if not greater importance of the fuller utilization of old forms and of limited amounts of energy, as well as the progress made in the avoidance of waste, may be inadequately appreciated. The availability of energy depends not merely on the number of forms of energy tapped or on the amounts of energy resources which are being utilized; it depends even more on the care and efficiency with which these available supplies are being utilized. It has been said that, in a material sense, the greatest progress may be expected not from the country which possesses the largest coal deposits, but from the country which uses its coal most efficiently and most wisely. But what is wise and efficient use? That is a difficult question which ties up with a large number of intangible and seemingly unrelated elements. It cannot be answered by a one-sided study of physical availability or an engineer's appraisal of efficiency or an economist's calculation of profitableness. An increase in the amount of energy generated or the shift to a new source of energy, taken by themselves, cannot adequately measure the progress of civilization, as will now be demonstrated.[2]

In "normal" times in the United States, incredible amounts of energy are generated, mostly from coal and oil, but also of the "elbow grease" variety. Much of it, however, may be lost in creating and maintaining a plant capacity which will never be used—misdirected investment, evil fruits of competition misunderstood and maladjusted.

On the other hand, one can well imagine a period in Roman history during which no increased energy was made available but which nevertheless was marked by remarkable progress along material lines. This seemingly paradoxical situation might be due to what Fairgrieve calls "momentum." But it may also be traceable to the establishment of law and order, to a better solution of social problems, to the extension of Roman institutions to other parts of the Empire. The mere expansion of the Empire might under certain circumstances mean additional progress; for larger areas permit the wider application of the principles of specialization and division of labor, principles which render the available physical resources more productive. As a matter of fact, when during the fourth century after Christ a new source of energy was being tapped and the use

[2] If in this discussion of resources in general and of energy resources in particular more space is devoted to the analysis of physical, technical, and material aspects, this does not mean that the importance of intangible factors is inadequately realized. The one-sided emphasis on the tangible is natural because its effects are more clearly discernible and more readily appraised than are the intangible. It is conceded that eras when human progress was greatest along spiritual lines may well have resulted in greater progress both relatively and absolutely, measured in both immaterial and material ways. It is possible that the commercial revolution advanced man proportionately as much as did the mechanical revolution, in spite of the fact that no new source of energy was being attacked but old forms were being used more effectively. The importance of the physical and mechanical is often overestimated.

of water wheels in flour milling and similar operations spread, the net result in terms of social progress was probably negative. Large numbers of workers lost their employment, and the resultant social conflict rendered the gain from the expanding energy control highly problematic. As always, one must distinguish between gross income and net profit. That distinction is valid not only in balancing the books of a business enterprise, but also in appraising the energy economy of an entire civilization.

The effect of expanding areas tapped in correlated effort, especially of expanding markets, on increased productivity was perhaps most pronounced during the period which began around the year 1500 and which is generally called the commercial revolution. Expanding trade areas led to a regional specialization, that is, a division of labor along the lines of natural advantages such as climate, mineral wealth, soils, etc., possessed by different peoples. As we stressed before, probably the greatest factor making for increased productivity is the specialization which permits the fuller use of the peculiar aptitudes of man and enables the people of different regions to specialize in the tasks best suited to the peculiarities of their habitat and congenial to their tastes, attitudes, etc. Commerce goes far to promote this specialization. In short, not the gross supply of energy but the manner of utilization counts most.

Energy History

To the future historian energy history probably will appear divided into three great periods or ages: the age of predominant dependence on animate energy, the age of inanimate energy derived mainly from the exhaustible fossil fuels, and the age of inanimate energy derived from continuous sources such as direct solar radiation, tidal power, carbon dioxide, etc. We are now living in the second age, the age of fossil fuels, which began sometime in the eighteenth century and is now rushing to its end with accelerating speed.

It was a great event when James Watt patented his steam engine in 1776, an event comparable to that when Prometheus snatched fire from Olympus. It marked the beginning of a long series of inventions, including the steam turbine, the gasoline explosion engine, the Diesel engine, the gas combustion turbine, the different jets, the water turbine, and a host of others which have made electricity one of the most widely used forms of energy. The steam engine was the first of a long and lengthening line of prime movers which harness the elementary forces of nature. These basic inventions in the field of energy use led to a vast number of other inventions which made possible the application of inanimate energy to industry, agriculture, transport, and communication. What is more, they so raised the productivity of man that he at last found the leisure and surplus which made possible the systematic pursuit of scientific research. Mechanization and science are twin forces which have changed and are changing man's environment.

It seems strange to think of mankind as having lived on this planet for countless generations in poverty and fear without tapping the vast funds of stored-up solar radiation in the form of coal, oil, and gas, or making use of the considerable power of falling water (except in mere trickles). The human race was like a poor family living in a hovel, under whose dirt floor was buried a huge treasure chest which promised the lucky owner vast wealth and power. If people knew of its existence, they did not have the key to open the lock. That key was provided by James Watt, and when the lock finally was opened, in Sombart's picturesque language "the earth became pregnant with new earths."[3]

So vast was this newly found treasure that at first man considered it limitless. But after a couple of hundred years of accelerated and increasing expenditures, the bottom of the treasure chest, although not yet visible, is suspected to lie not too far below the present tapping zone.

So accustomed has man become to the use of the vast inanimate powers derived from the fossil fuels, to the joys of expanding and upward-surging enterprise, to dependence on countless robots, docile serfs that do not speak back, that even the realization of an impending collapse cannot retard the speed with which the top spins.

So great is the confidence of modern industrial man in his own capacity to create resources, to discover ways and means of tapping new sources of energy, of finding treasure chests buried more deeply than that containing the fossil fuels, that he insists on keeping up the exhausting pace of fuel use. If, as seems possible, an increasing share of the vast energies now derived from exhaustible

[3] Werner Sombart, *Der Moderne Kapitalismus*, Dunker and Humblot, München and Leipzig, 1928.

fuels is used to discover ways of tapping new and inexhaustible energies, that confidence may well be justified. Much will depend on the continuation of peace.

Miracle of the Fossil Fuel Age

If it were possible to give a full account of developments in the realm of energy use from the time when the first satisfactory steam engine was perfected to the present, the story would read like a fairy tale. If one realizes that at the beginning of the period only a few million tons of coal a year were produced as compared with about three billion tons today, that little oil was produced before the middle of the last century as compared with nearly eight billion barrels a year today, that the first electric power station was built in the early eighties whereas electricity output today is measured by the hundreds of billions of kilowatt-hours, that the natural gas industry is virtually a newcomer and the atomic energy industry a mere infant, and if one further considers that all these energies require for their harnessing and use vast amounts of metals extracted from far vaster amounts of ore, he will get a dim notion of the miraculous performance of the past two hundred years.

But, as was stated before, the fossil-fuel-based phase of the machine age is driving with irresistible force toward its end. Exhaustion of fossil fuel reserves now appears nearer than had been anticipated. What will follow? No one knows, but those most competent to predict point to the possibilities of tapping the vast and inexhaustible supplies of direct solar radiation and other continuous sources of energy.

We cannot believe that this fossil-fuel era in which we live, an era which may soon start its climactic approach to exhaustion, will be regarded by historians of the future as a period in which energy has been uniquely abundant. Instead, there is every reason to expect that succeeding eras will provide still greater abundance of energy from our constant sources. In the meantime, there is a lot of work to be done. Within a few decades a good start must have been made toward the new systems of energy production and consumption; and while this goes on, our technological rear guard will be engaged in retarding in every possible way the corrosive growth of our energy losses.[4]

[4] Eugene E. Ayres, "Major Sources of Energy," a paper read during the 28th annual meeting of the American Petroleum Institute, November 9, 1948, p. 138.

DISTRIBUTION OF MINERALS

In general this miracle of the mechanical revolution was confined to the West—western Europe and North America. There is a strange contrast in the geographical distribution of men and of robots on the face of the earth. The robot population is not distributed proportionately to the human population. On the contrary, it appears that the density of the robot population tends to vary inversely with that of the human population. This conclusion is far from accurate, for the diversity of natural endowment and cultural development in different regions of the earth materially affects the existence of robots.[5]

To trace this uneven distribution of robots to the uneven geographical distribution of minerals would be a gross oversimplification of a highly complex relationship. It would be mineral determinism, a most naïve variety of environmentalism. For one thing, some people, especially the English-speaking peoples, exploit minerals that lie in other people's territories. Others, like the Russians, have just begun to exploit their minerals systematically. Actually, the distribution of robots is the result of the play of the myriad of currents and crosscurrents which we call history.

IMPLICATIONS OF THE MECHANICAL REVOLUTION

The Mechanical Revolution as a Cultural Revolution

The substitution of mechanical energy from dead substances such as coal, petroleum, natural gas, or of the gravitational energy of falling water, for the muscular energy generated by men and beasts in return for food consumed, is a change so radical that it has altered the very design of civilization beyond recognition. The alteration, however, is neither complete nor perfect, for the material transformation, both technical and economic, demands a reorientation in the realm of the mind and the spirit too sudden and too drastic to be performed adequately and smoothly.

The old machinery, not only of material civilization but of the most refined cultural patterns as well, was designed to meet the

[5] See the discussion of population density as contrasted with the man-land ratio in chap. 8.

great emergency of an ever-growing population pushing with increased vigor and rising impatience against the subsistence levels of the earth. Man faced a chronic condition of scarcity of food, of land, of everything. The inevitableness of scarcity had yielded to the possibility of plenty; at times even overwhelming superabundance threatened. Therefore the machinery of social and economic institutions had to be adjusted to new dangers. Philosophy, which had long served as a means of escape from the limitations of human abilities, has had to make an about-face to meet the needs of the new Prometheus who feels his powers as clearly as the old Adam realized his limitations. The positive attitude toward population increase which was demanded in the agricultural world because of the need for labor and markets had to be reversed to meet the emergence of technological unemployment and the man-replacing power of machines. Agriculture, for millenniums the backbone of civilized life, lost its primacy and was forced to takes its place behind mining, manufacturing, commerce, and finance. Thus the mechanical revolution necessarily involved a social revolution, a revolution in every field of human thought and action.

The Mechanical Revolution a Gradual Shift

At this point we must pause to forestall a misunderstanding. To say that the mechanical revolution is a shift from muscular to mechanical energy is to do violence to the finer meaning of words. For the word "revolution" denotes something sudden, whereas a shift is more apt to be slow and gradual. It would be more accurate, therefore, to speak of the mechanical *evolution* rather than the mechanical revolution, for three reasons. In the first place, the difference between ancient and modern energy usage is one of degree rather than of essence, for even the most primitive man used some inanimate energy. He did so when he ran downhill, when he floated downstream on a log, when he cooked his food over a fire. The ancients in their mining operations frequently took advantage of the expansion and shrinkage caused by changing temperatures. In building their pyramids, the Egyptians made use of gravitation in the most ingenious way. Furthermore, their priests used steam power to operate the heavy temple doors—and incidentally to awe the multitude who marveled at the miracle. The use of wind power is as old as history. But if the difference between ancient and modern energy usage is one only of degree, it is so drastic as to be in effect a difference of essence.

In the second place, the shift to the modern usage, when it did come, came gradually and not without careful preparations and forebodings. In a very real sense, James Watt stood on the shoulders of the great but forgotten men who invented the simple machines, to say nothing of the da Vincis and Newcomens who had invented simple steam engines. His work was prompted by the evil effects of forest depletion. Without the commercial revolution, the mechanical revolution is hardly thinkable. Furthermore the Renaissance, Humanism, and even the Crusades prepared the soil.

Third, when the mechanical revolution got under way, it spread very gradually from its starting point in the coal-producing regions of England to the rest of the Occident and still more gradually to the world at large. The application of steam power to water pumps in coal mines and of water power in textile mills was the first definite symptom. Gradually the use of steam spread to manufacturing and to transportation on land and sea. Then Fourneyron invented the modern water turbine. That secret force called electricity was next harnessed as a source of light, heat, and power—first in small plants here and there, later boldly in giant plants and in superpower zones. The gas motor followed, extending mechanical locomotion to the air and emancipating land transportation from the limits of the steel rail. The long-distance transmission of electricity was cheapened, new sources of energy were tapped, and old ones used better. Used in ever new forms, in ever wider areas, in ever better ways, mechanical energy waxes in power for good and for evil, a product of time rather than of man, a living force rather than a dead tool. As the development over which no one seems to have any control proceeds at an accelerated pace, its influence over man and his civilization grows cumulatively. Old institutions wither under its burning breath; new institutions rise.

Old and New Resource Patterns

While the mechanical revolution is evolutionary in its origin and growth, it is revolutionary in effect. It has remade the resource basis of human civilization, at least of western civilization. Before James Watt started the definite shift from animate to inanimate energy, the entire civilized world had been using the same ancient resource pattern. Solar radiation was used almost exclusively in its most common form, sunshine. This, in turn, was used mainly for agricultural purposes in conjunction with water and with soil—in part, at least, a fund of stored-up solar radiation. The chief use which can be made of the products of agriculture is to feed men and beasts. Food and feed generate animate energy, the most important—in fact, almost the only—form in which energy is available in the ancient resource pattern.

The modern resource pattern which the white man is superimposing on this ancient pattern rests on a different and superior energy basis. The generation of steam power makes available to man a source of energy which, in the course of time, proves progressively superior to the animate energy obtained from food and feed. Man has relatively little control over the metabolism by which food is turned into energy in living organisms. With the aid of scientific dietetics he may somewhat improve the energy yield from a given amount of food or feed, but only within narrow limits. Moreover, food and feed production are subject to the law of diminishing returns. On the other hand, man can consciously improve the energy output of coal and other sources of inanimate energy.

Static Nature of Vegetable Civilization

Hence an economy using animate energy is basically static; an economy using inanimate energy is essentially dynamic. This, to be sure, has only relative validity. In their formative stages the economies depending on animate energy—the vegetable civilizations, as they are aptly called—were probably as dynamic as our civilization is now. It is perhaps no exaggeration to say that a greater advance was made by man before the mechanical revolution than since. On the other hand, it would seem possible that, at some future stage, economies using inanimate energy—machine civilizations, in other words—may likewise reach a static equilibrium. In fact, as will be developed later on, machine civilization, as at present constituted, rests on a less permanent basis than does vegetable civilization.

Moreover, it should not be assumed that a dynamic economy or civilization is necessarily superior to a static economy or civilization. In this case, however, the assumption of superiority seems justified, for a civilization based on inanimate energy seems to offer better chances of reaching greater heights of human achievement than one based on animate energy. If man does not avail himself of these chances, the blame rests on him, not on the kind of energy utilized. To enter into a discussion of the criteria of a "better" civilization would be the height of folly, for the determination of what is "better" involves judgment, opinion, subjective appraisal. What seems "better" to the Asiatic may be detestable to the Occidental, and vice versa.

SUPERIORITY OF INANIMATE ENERGY

Viewed in a material sense and measured in terms of economic efficiency, the civilization based on the modern resource pattern is superior to that based on the ancient resource pattern. Its superior efficiency rests on the greater ease with which a surplus over and above the minimum sustenance required to support the population can be produced. The capacity to accumulate such a surplus is dependent on three factors: (1) the amount of "free" energy available, (2) the efficient use made of the available energy, and (3) the rational control of population growth.

Advantage of "Free" Energy

Animate energy is energy produced by a living organism—an animal or a plant. To be able to live and work, an organism must take in food. Animate energy, therefore, is energy derived from food. If this food is the spontaneous product of sunshine, rainfall, virgin soil fertility, and other untransformed aspects of nature, the energy derived from it may also be said to be a spontaneous product of nature and therefore free energy. If, however, the food must first be produced by man with the aid of animals bred by him and of tools made by him, animate energy is to a high degree an artificial man-made product. In that case the energy spent in producing the necessary food and feed and tools must be deducted from the total energy derived from the food before the net energy available for work can be ascertained. Since, under civilized conditions, most foods and feeds are not spontaneous products of untransformed nature but the result of past energy expenditure, most animate energy is not a net addition to the energy supply available to man. It is normally assumed that the energy derived from food and feed exceeds that required to produce the food and feed—in other words, that at least some of it represents a "net" product.

Whether that assumption is justified depends on animal metabolism, on the efficiency of the productive system; and this, in turn, depends largely on the quality of the natural agents utilized and the amount of surplus which can be accumulated. An intelligent, educated, healthy farmer working good land under favorable climatic conditions, using good tools and applying good techniques, is apt to produce food and feed capable of yielding energy far in excess of that used in producing the food and feed. His net product, then, is large. On the other hand, a dull and inexperienced farmer, tilling poor land under unfavorable climatic conditions and applying faulty techniques, is apt to produce food and feed capable of yielding an amount of energy hardly—if at all—in excess of that required to produce the food and feed. Virgin soil, fertility, and good climate are untransformed aspects of nature; so are native good health and ability. But education, tools, techniques, and improved hygienic conditions are cultural additions to the natural environment. They are the product of former net products of energy. Hence, an energetic, vigorous, intelligent population occupying fertile land topographically and climatically well situated, being able to produce great "net" products, will be able to use these "net" products to improve their tools and techniques and to spread education, and thus cumulatively add to their advantages. The other group will be held, if not pulled down, by the vicious circle of their initial handicap. Whatever the theoretical explanation of the superiority of inanimate over animate energy may be, the fact of its superiority is hardly disputable. The following statement furnishes strong supporting evidence:

Advantages of Mineral Energy. Whether delivered as electricity to the farm or factory, produced under the hood of an automobile, or generated in the hold of the *Queen Mary*, mineral energy provides a greater concentration of power than could the most ingenious and efficient use of untold human and animal labor. And mineral energy provides power in a more convenient, compact, mobile, and controllable form. The famous "Borax 20 Mule Team" reached a speed of six to eight miles an hour. It was probably the biggest sum of animal power ever brought under the control of a single driver—outside of the circus. But the frailest of women drives around today with three times as much lethal horsepower, and a potential ninety miles an hour under the hood . . .

The greatest advantage of mineral energy is that it is cheap as compared with animal or human energy. Cost is crucial. Many forms of energy have never been used because they cost too much to harness to practical uses. Wind power, for example, is both unlimited and free, but costly to use. Similarly, we have not learned a practical way of using atomic energy for peaceful purposes.

Compared to machines, men and animals are costly. The upkeep is too high. Any farmer will tell you that horses spend more time standing around eating their heads off than working. Men have to be fed, clothed, and sheltered. That is why even slave labor is not cheap. Our mechanical slaves get along on cheaper "food" and require less attention than either men or animals. Aside from the morals involved, the use of forced human labor is a sure sign of industrial backwardness.

. . . On the whole, animal energy probably costs thirty to a hundred times as much as mineral energy, and human energy from three hundred to a thousand times as much. No wonder we waste everything but man power! . . . No wonder Americans are accused of being demons for speed and efficiency. In purely practical terms, we want to get the most out of our costly man power, so we devise mechanical marvels to replace it, supplement it, augment it, and conserve it.[6]

Animate Energy and Proliferation

Before the mechanical revolution few farming peoples were in the enviable position of the more favorably situated. We find them in China during certain periods of her history, we find them in Egypt, in Mesopotamia; but those less favorably situated may be said to have been in the majority. Generally speaking, therefore, before the mechanical revolution agriculture was a fairly hopeless undertaking. It was carried on after a fashion in a vicious circle which prevented its rising above a certain dead level of mere vegetation and proliferation. People raised food and feed one day to generate the energy to raise more food and feed the next. If, by chance, a surplus was achieved, one of two things happened. Either a powerful upper class usurped the surplus, or the human and

[6] Gloria Waldron and J. Frederic Dewhurst, *Power, Machines, and Plenty,* Public Affairs Pamphlet No. 142, 1948, pp. 11–12. Largely based on J. Frederic Dewhurst and associates, *America's Needs and Resources,* Twentieth Century Fund, New York, 1947.

animal population simply rose to the point where the dead level was struck again. On the whole, people raised food to generate the energy required to raise the food. In the meantime they lived. But what for?

Inanimate energy differs essentially from animate energy. Genetically speaking, the energy lodged in a ton of coal is closely akin to the energy in a ton of corn or wheat or hay. Both came from the sun; but here the similarity ends, for coal is the product of past solar radiation; it was made ages ago—before the advent of man. At any rate, it was made without any expenditure of human energy. It is there ready to be used. Not so the corn, hay, oats, wheat, meat, and other feed and food from which animate energy is derived. To be sure, they too are products of solar radiation, but of current, not ancient, prehistoric, sunshine. Since Adam's expulsion from Paradise, sunshine has produced crops only when man helps. All solar radiation is free energy, and the sun is the only source of free energy available to man. The sun produced both the coal and the food; but while coal, petroleum, and natural gas are undiluted sunshine and therefore sources of totally free energy, food and feed, having been produced with the aid of man at the expenditure of animate energy, are not.

The fact that most coal is found some distance below the ground and must therefore be mined, whereas feed and food crops develop on the surface, is merely incidental. Food and feed as well as coal—nowadays at least—must be moved, coal vertically and horizontally, food and feed mainly horizontally. In other words, to be available for use, both coal and feed must be transported, and transportation requires energy. In this respect they are alike; but here again coal enjoys an inherent advantage, for if coal is raised and transported with the aid of coal it may be said to raise and move itself. We may use up the coal reserves more quickly, but the coal available for energy production over and above transportation is still a net product. On the other hand a ton of hay moved by an ox is not a net product, for the ox that draws it must eat, but the coal that generates the steam to pull the train does not.

Energy and the Function of Land

Since animate energy can be derived only from food and feed, any economy built on it must be predominantly an agricultural economy, a vegetable civilization. This term applies even where animals play an important part, for animals live on vegetable matter. In a vegetable civilization land means wealth—land in the sense of surface, standing room, soil, the recipient of rainfall and sunshine, the natural agent for the commutation of matter. Feudalism—the system in which social status and economic as well as political power are proportionate to property holdings in the sense of landed rights—is the typical form of social control found in the agricultural economies of the Occident and of Japan. In other sections, especially in the monsoon regions of southeastern Asia, the strategic significance of water has vitally affected the control pattern. Still different patterns have evolved in other areas, but land as the source of vegetable growth is always the foundation on which economies using animate energy must build.

Since empty land is worthless, the landowner wants to see his land inhabited, he wants people to increase in numbers. His is a strong positive population policy. Birth control does not fit into his scheme. To yield a surplus to the lord or a subsistence to the peasant, land must be cultivated. The defense no less than the conquest of land requires man power. Thus, in vegetable civilizations, policy is dominated by land hunger and man hunger. Under those circumstances people tend to breed to the subsistence level; if an area is filled up, migration or colonization elsewhere or war or pestilence re-establishes the equilibrium between man and land.

Energy and Labor Efficiency

In ancient times, human labor was relatively ineffective. The lower classes were abused by tribute-levying conquerors, heavily taxed by their own rulers, held in bondage, or even actually enslaved. The masses of the people were ignorant and generally lacked proper training. The profit incentive and the stimulating hope of economic and political advancement were absent. Ineffectiveness is self-perpetuating. The inefficient worker, producing little or no surplus over and above the means of sustenance, cannot improve his capital equipment. At times, what little surplus could be coaxed from the toiling masses in the form of tribute or taxes was squandered by the ruling leisure class. Measured by modern standards, a worker inadequately supported by capital equipment is generally an ineffective producer. Not being able to produce and spare that which could raise his effectiveness, he is caught in a vicious circle.

In general, this condition continued until the mechanical revolution radically altered production methods. To be sure, peasant agriculture in certain sections of the world accomplished remarkable results; and in the cities craftsmanship, in some respects, reached heights never surpassed in the machine civilization. Yet, on the whole, productive effectiveness, measured by present standards, lagged far behind.

Moreover, before the mechanical revolution the life and health of workers were not guarded with the care characteristic of our modern industrial civilization. The economic value of good health is self-evident, but that of increased life expectancy is less so. Its most important economic implication is the resultant improvement of the ratio of the nonproductive to the productive period of human life. If we take 15 years as the nonproductive period of childhood, a man who dies at the age of 30 represents the balance between the productive and nonproductive years. At 45 the ratio of productive to nonproductive labor is 2 to 1; at 60, 3 to 1, etc. The average expectancy of life in this country at present is about 70, whereas up to about 150 years ago it was probably somewhere between 30 and 40.

Because of the ineffective production methods of pre-industrial days, entire families—men, women, and children—kept busy from morning till night during the working season to raise the necessities of life. There was no time for study or schooling. As a result, labor lacked ambition and had little chance to shake off the curse of inefficiency. However, this statement must not be misinterpreted. Within the limits set by the ancient resource pattern, a Chinese may reach the highest possible position of achievement. His knowledge of plant life, of soils and fertilizers may be as complete as our knowledge of atoms and electrons, of electricity and radioactivity —or even more so—but the effectiveness of his knowledge is reduced by the inherent defects of his system. Moreover, ignorance breeds superstition, and superstition puts innumerable obstacles in the way of progress. Being ineffective and ignorant, man had no hope. Religion therefore took on a "defeatist" character, an "otherworldliness" which acted as an opiate, not as a stimulant. Asceticism developed, which taught man to seek contentment simply by not wanting, by stifling his wants and desires.

Energy and Capital Requirements

It must be conceded that the oxcart is a simple device, compared with the train drawn by a diesel locomotive over steel rails. A wheelwright can build an oxcart, but the train and rails cannot be made without blast furnaces, steel mills, and many other complex devices. Hence, the efficient utilization of inanimate energy requires large indirect and roundabout expenditures of energy. A huge array of capital equipment must be created, maintained, enlarged, and improved. But here again it must be kept in mind that this capitalistic equipment is created out of inanimate, that is, free energy; it contributes to the fuller and better use of inanimate energy; it too may be said to create itself just as the coal was said to raise itself. To be sure, if the equipment did not have to be built, either less coal, petroleum, etc., would have to be produced to yield man a given amount of ultimate consumers' goods, or more ultimate consumers' goods would have to be made available. But the ability to yield a surplus is not materially affected. In other words, an economy based on inanimate energy requires a larger overhead, but the overhead can be more easily created; in fact, to a certain extent it creates itself.

Moreover, animate energy calls for a considerable overhead, though for different reasons. In the first place, animals must not only eat but they must also sleep or rest. They pass through a preparatory stage during which they eat and rest, but do not work. Furthermore, they get sick and grow old. So besides feed, shelter must be provided, and care for the young, feeble, and sick. The same applies to human beings. If we assume that eight out of twenty-four hours is a normal working period, continuous operation would require three shifts of animals. The overhead expense, especially the item for shelter, is therefore disproportionately large in the case of animate energy. The extra expense of taking care of the animals and men during the nonworking periods of life—youth, old age, and sickness—is somewhat counterbalanced by the necessity of keeping machines and engines in reserve. Keeping three shifts of animals or men simultaneously engaged in a given task is frequently out of the question. It certainly was impossible before artificial light was provided to make night work possible, and that is an accomplishment of machine civilization.

Energy and the Choice of Materials

In origin and use, animate energy is more closely related to organic matter—vegetable and animal substances—than to inorganic. As was pointed out before, the use of animate energy precludes the use of more than small and easily accessible amounts of minerals, especially metals. Only a small portion of the minerals exploited today is found on or near the surface; most of them are found at some depth below. So long as only man and animal power is available to work the pumps, the ventilators, the hoists, etc., the limits of mining operations are closely drawn. Moreover, hand-hewn and hand-picked minerals are essentially products of human labor and therefore belong to the animate energy cycle. Only when steam power makes deep shafts and large mining operations technically possible can metals come into their own. The limitation of the metal supply hinders other operations. The limit in the usable size of a vegetable or fiber rope with its poor ratio of weight to tensile strength is reached long before that of a modern steel cable. Oil drilling now reaches depths of 10,000 feet and more. A fiber rope of this length would break under its own weight; moreover, it could not resist the heat. The same principle applies to construction above ground. High structures can be built of stone and even of brick, as is shown by the pyramids, the Tower of Babel, the Chinese Wall, the Zikkurat, and other ancient monuments. But these mineral structures of antiquity, which were built with animate energy supported only by simple machines, represented unique products of their respective civilizations, each of which was capable of producing only one or a few. Some of them almost drained the resources of their makers. Such structures, therefore, were not representative. The typical structure of ancient civilization clearly reflects the limitations of both animate energy and organic matter. A wooden beam used in construction cannot extend beyond a certain length without undue loss of strength. This places a limit on many things—on the size of tools, of machines, of vehicles, of furnaces, of factories, etc. This limitation on the size and strength of organic matter in turn reacted unfavorably on the units of energy that could be employed. The number of oxen that can be effectively used to draw a load limits the load, but the size of the vehicle that can be constructed from wood also limits the number of oxen. Suppose the Romans could have mined coal without steam to modernize metal mining; the use of coal would still have been limited, for without metal they could not have built furnaces big and strong enough to keep the fury of combustion in check. Animate energy limits the choice of material and thus largely precludes the use of inanimate energy.[7]

An Example of Limitations. One of the best examples of the limitations of organic matter is the wooden ship. By about the seventeenth century the wooden ship, after slow evolution in size, strength, speed, etc., seemed to have reached the highest level of perfection possible under the limitations of organic matter, i.e., wood. In the British "ship of the line" no noticeable improvements appeared possible so long as ships were built of wood. The limitations of the organic manifested themselves in numerous ways. The length of the ship depends largely on the size of the rudder, for its size determines the power to maneuver the ship. The size of the rudder, in turn, depends on the size of the sternpost, the strategic piece of wood in which ribs or sides are anchored and to which the rudder is attached. The sternpost was a single block of wood fashioned out of the largest and strongest oak trees available. By their size, therefore, oak trees set a limit to the size of the sternpost, through it to the size of the rudder, and, in turn, through the latter to the length of the ship. Moreover, by their number, oak trees limited the size of the fleet. The admirals would clamor for more ships; Samuel Pepys, as Secretary of the Admiralty, would scour the land for sternposts. Again and again, plans for enlargement of the fleet and for campaigns had to be given up for the simple reason that there were not enough mature oak trees. Oaks were considered mature at about 90 years of age, and there was no way of speeding up the slow process of growth.

Masts were another limiting factor. They were made from the

---

[7] It may be mentioned that in some vegetable civilizations a somewhat mystical attitude toward metals develops. For example, metal plowshares are blamed for crop failures; and the blacksmith is a semilegendary character—feared, despised, and honored alike.

tallest straight trees—generally firs, pines, and other conifers—that could be found from Volhynia to New England. Their size and strength materially affected both the size and the speed of the wooden ship.

Another bottleneck was the so-called compass wood, i.e., pieces of wood taken out of the crotches where branches came out of the tree trunk. These extra-strong pieces were needed to join vital parts, such as decks and sides. Trees were bandaged to increase artificially the numbers of compass pieces which a tree would yield.

As soon as iron and, later, steel, especially alloy steel, were substituted for wood, the size of the ship increased by leaps and bounds. Metal permitted the presence of fire and thus the use of steam. To be sure, metals too have their limits, but these are set much higher and to a degree can be pushed forward by scientific and technological improvements.

Energy, Materials, Accuracy, and Scale of Production

The miracle of modern production is to a large extent explained by the scale of mass production. This in turn rests on the interchangeability of parts, and this interchangeability depends on the accuracy with which parts are machined. Wood cannot be worked accurately enough to make wooden parts interchangeable. Accuracy that permits interchangeability is possible only with metal. Animate energy and wood go together, and inanimate energy goes with metals. The use of metals permits increasing accuracy. Here is an intriguing account of this development.

There was the watch, an intricate mechanism made up of springs, gears and small screws. And its effectiveness or ability to tell the time depended on the accurate duplication of the parts. We know a good time keeper must be equipped with accurate gears having the required number of teeth, equally spaced. The cost and difficulty of making gears were the chief factors that prevented everyone's having a watch. At the beginning of the 18th century a machine was built by a Frenchman to automatically divide a circular metal blank into equal parts and cut properly shaped teeth. Along about the same period another French watchmaker devised another remarkable machine—a lathe for cutting the threads on small metal screws used in watches. It was also equipped with an attachment to turn tapered parts very similar to that used on modern machine tools. As a result of these new machines watches became more numerous.

Thus it was the French who with the aid of their clock and watch-making machines opened up a new era in manufacturing. Some of these ideas crossed the English Channel and were perfected and expanded in connection with an entirely different product—the steam engine.

In the early 18th century, when the French inventors were developing machines to make accurate watches, the English were faced with a shortage of mine labor. This was very important in a country having little wood for fuel. One of the difficulties in mining coal was pumping the water from the mines. In an effort to solve this problem Thomas Newcomen developed an atmospheric steam pumping engine, which utilized atmospheric pressure to move a piston which in turn operated the mine pump.

During the next fifty years many of these engines were built to pump out mines and the design remained essentially unchanged until a small model of a Newcomen engine fell into the hands of James Watt, a Scotch instrument maker. When he saw the model, Watt was struck with the idea of using steam at greater than atmospheric pressure to move the piston of the engine instead of condensing the steam under the piston and letting the smaller atmospheric pressure do the work as in the Newcomen engine.

He made several small models, proving to himself he was on the right track. But when he tried to build a full-size engine he came face to face with a production problem. He realized that to maintain the efficiency of his new steam engine the piston would have to fit the cylinder snugly to prevent the high-pressure steam from leaking by. He gave the job to a Mr. Smeaton who was recognized as one of the best mechanics in the country. Smeaton made a cylinder a foot and a half in diameter, but it was *three-eighths of an inch out of round,* which made it useless for holding the steam pressure when a piston was fitted to it.

However, another Englishman, John Wilkinson, came to his rescue with a new idea for guiding the tool to cut a more perfect circle—the boring bar principle so well known in production today. By this method they made a new cylinder that was only one-sixteenth of an inch eccentric and was quite satisfactory. Step by step ingenious men were discovering the rewards of accuracy and uncovering new ways of achieving it. Thus the steam engine opened up a new source of power and its applications revolutionized the century-old methods of laborious hand work, at the same time providing more things for more people.[8]

Thus the shift from animate energy to inanimate energy meant the shift from organic to inorganic work materials and brought in its turn interchangeability of parts and the modern methods of mass production.

Energy and Speed of Production

One of the greatest advantages of the modern production process that utilizes inanimate energy is the speed with which work can be done. A comparison betwen an ancient and a modern construction job drives home the advantages of speed. If we assume that the building of an Egyptian pyramid required the work of 50,000 slaves for 20 years, while a skyscraper of comparable size can be built by 5000 laborers in six months, the number of workers at a given moment is as 10 is to 1; but if the time element is taken into account, the ratio is 400 to 1. This means that it took approximately 400 times as much food to generate the man power that built the pyramid as it took to feed the workers who built the skyscraper. For Egyptian farmers to raise that surplus food over and above their own requirements was no small tax on their agricultural skill,[9] for whereas American agriculture enjoys the benefits of considerable support by inanimate energy, Egyptian agriculture suffered from its very dependence on animate energy. Both the pyramid and the skyscraper require considerable outside work and fixed investments: quarries, roads, rafts, derricks, etc., in Egypt; mines, mills, railroads, engines, machines, etc., in the United States. While the American equipment is infinitely larger and more complex than the Egyptian, it is also more efficient. Moreover, most of the American equipment is relatively permanent and versatile. It is used to build many skyscrapers and numerous other objects, whereas most of the Egyptian equipment served solely the task of building one par-

---

[8] C. F. Kettering and Allen Orth, *American Battle for Abundance,* © 1947, General Motors Corporation, Detroit, pp. 12–14.

[9] In antiquity Egyptian agriculture was decidedly more seasonal than it is now. In so far as the building of pyramids took place during the dormant season, the problem mentioned here solved itself to some extent. This consideration, however, does not detract from the validity of the case as illustrating the relative efficiency of animate and inanimate energy.

ticular pyramid. Thus it is an open question which construction job required more overhead—the pyramid or the skyscraper.

Finally, agricultural work is drawn out because of seasonal interruptions. In most areas where agriculture flourishes, all work more or less comes to a standstill during the winter. Moreover, during the growing period weeks may go by during which man can do no more than watch nature take its course. But man and beast must live throughout the year, and the equipment must be kept in condition. Thus for numerous reasons, the fixed charges or overhead costs in vegetable civilization, while not large in absolute amounts, are very considerable when expressed in proportion to the actual work performed.

Energy and Mobility

One of the most important uses of energy is locomotion—the moving of things and people and ideas from place to place. The lack of suitable and adequate energy condemns vegetable civilizations to do without locomotion beyond a very limited range. Transportation in vegetable civilizations is hopelessly inefficient. The inefficiency applies to the road, the vehicle, and the motive power. The energy required to transport heavy and bulky goods in wooden vehicles drawn by animals over poorly built roads is so great, and the food or feed consumption necessary to yield the energy is so large, that only short distances can be negotiated.[10] Primitive water transportation requires less energy per ton-mile than land transportation. Moreover, water transportation, utilizing the river currents or wind, may be said to be partly emancipated from the limitations of animate energy. It may suffer because of insufficient control over the inanimate energy used and therefore it may not be comparable to modern water transportation. Furthermore, being confined to rivers and bays and coastal waters, it can affect only small portions of an area. Yet the construction of the Imperial Canal which brought tribute rice from southern China to the capital of the north, avoiding the pirate-infested coastal waters, proves the im-

[10] Cf. O. E. Baker, "Transportation in China," *Annals of the American Academy of Political and Social Science,* November, 1930, pp. 160–161; also W. H. Mallory, *China, Land of Famine,* Special Publication No. 6, American Geographical Society, New York, 1926, pp. 29–35, especially p. 33.

portance which may be attached to inland water transportation even in vegetable civilizations.

Efficient land transportation, however, is essentially a product of the mechanical revolution: steam power, gas explosion, electricity, turbines, diesel engines, dynamos, duraluminum, alloy steel, cement, machine-built concrete roads, railroads, automobiles, and airplanes—all these are products of the new age; they have made transportation what it is—cheap, swift, and efficient on land, by water, and in the air. The same holds true of communication. It is a commonplace to say that modern transportation and communication have completely changed the basis of civilization.

Their aid enables the mechanized civilization to beat the vegetable civilization at its own game, for they have made possible a fuller utilization of solar radiation by agriculture. Farmers whom the mechanical revolution has endowed with mobility can move to the sunshine even if it is far from market and from water. Power, water, and fertilizers can be brought to them and their products can be shipped to distant markets. Thus farms can spread out and their broad acres can drink in volumes of sunshine, while the peasants of immobile vegetable civilizations must huddle together on small garden patches and produce their crops by adding much labor to some sunshine instead of much sunshine to some labor. Mechanized mobility, moreover, has made possible the cultivation of the great steppes, the granaries of the modern world. They are steppes because their distance from the sea or the intervening mountain barriers shut off the climatic influences of the ocean; and hence they are essentially inaccessible if transportation depends on animate energy. Without the railroad and the steamship, the great steppes could not have gained their present significance in world food production.

Energy and Population Increase[11]

Above all, mobility spares the agriculture of the machine civilization one of the worst curses of vegetable civilization. It eliminates the fatal connection between food supply and birth rate which

[11] The relationship between resource patterns and population trends is more fully discussed in chap. 8. The remarks here should be interpreted in the light of the fuller discussion in that chapter.

was the fundamental weakness of ancient civilization. The fertility of a given piece of soil, the blessing of good climate—ample rain and sunshine, each in its time—can be utilized only by raising food. In China most food must be consumed where it is produced. Thus, immobility condemns a vegetable civilization to crowding—unless the basic natural advantages are to remain unused. But the food supply of a mechanized economy tied up with the world market by modern exchange is mobile. It does not need to be consumed on the spot; it can move thousands of miles to markets. Its worth to the producer through exchange can be turned into innumerable forms, none of which needs to promote population increase. Mechanized agriculture, therefore, is not only efficient in terms of per-man output, but also mobile. This mobility, however, applies not only to the agriculture of industrial countries but to their manufacturing industries as well. As a result, foreign trade and the export of capital assume increasing importance and thus broaden the resource basis of mobilized economy. We see, therefore, that the energy basis is truly the foundation of a civilization. It determines the choice of materials which can be utilized, it sets a definite limit to the size of performance, it governs the degree of mobility and, in general, controls the arts, societal and technical, and through them shapes the institutions, material and nonmaterial. In short, it largely determines the type of civilization and the resource pattern on which the civilization rests.

Drawbacks to the Use of Inanimate Energy

What has been said so far has all been in favor of the modern resource pattern. Now we must turn to the reverse side of the picture. For where there is light there must also be shadow; no advantage can be gained except at a price. The advantage of the modern system can be summarized as superior efficiency. The price paid for that advantage is security and permanency. As was pointed out above, the ancient resource pattern depends primarily on animate energy and hence on current solar radiation. The modern resource pattern is built around stored-up solar radiation—coal, petroleum, natural gas—a fund which is used up as it is used. Current solar radiation, on the other hand, is a flow, a perpetual succession of self-renewable supply units.

A civilization based on a fund of exhaustible resources cannot be permanent; it is necessarily a passing phenomenon in human history. A civilization based on a flow of renewable resources may be permanent. But fortunately inanimate energy can be derived not only from the fund of stored-up solar energy, but also from the flow of current solar energy. The ancient process which through photosynthesis produces plants which are used as food or feed to generate animate energy is not the only way in which current solar radiation can be utilized. Sunshine can also be turned into inanimate energy, either directly by the use of mirrors or indirectly by windmills, by power plants, by water turbines, etc. The ancient system depends one-sidedly on the animate energy drawn from sunshine, and the modern places undue reliance on the inanimate energy drawn from fossil fuels; the system of the future should utilize both and supplement them by turning sunshine into inanimate energy, thus reducing the strain on fossil fuels and postponing the day of their exhaustion.

The modern resource pattern lacks not only permanency but also security. On the one hand, the mechanized Occident shares with vegetable civilizations the dangers of natural disasters—floods, droughts, insect pests, etc.—although their frequency and rigor may have been reduced. On the other hand, both the complexity and the internationalization of the modern economy give rise to new dangers. A modern industrial civilization may be compared to a high pyramid of cultural and institutional development, erected on a relatively narrow basis of natural resources. It is daring, lofty, impressive. As long as the system of civilization runs smoothly its splendor is dazzling; but at the first shock of an earthquake it topples over. A vegetable civilization, on the other hand, is like a giant squatting on the ground in sodden safety. Napoleon could not conquer Russia, neither could the Germans or the Allies. The decisive defeat of the Russians at the hands of the Japanese in 1905 caused hardly a ripple in the huge ocean of humanity spread over the enormous area that was the Russian Empire. China still carries on after thousands of years, long after the proud structures of Greece and Rome[12] have crumbled to dust.

---

[12] Both Roman and Greek civilizations were attempts to build high commercial and political superstructures on relatively narrow resource bases which were composed largely of vegetable matter and animate energy, though reinforced by minerals.

However, insecurity is not an inherent defect of the modern resource pattern; it is incidental rather than basic, cultural rather than natural, institutional rather than technological; most of it springs from its pecuniary aspects, which are insufficiently adapted to the resource system. Money economy and the capitalistic spirit are institutional developments which the use of inanimate energy has greatly stimulated, but they probably are not the only institutional pattern which inanimate energy can produce. In their present make-up, they represent an undigested mixture of ancient tradition and modern developments. The troubles of today, therefore, are largely brought on by machines, but they are not the necessary results of inanimate energy.

Finally, modern machine civilization may be unduly dynamic, just as the ancient pattern is unduly static. One system suffers from lack of change; the other, from too much and too rapid change. Up to a certain point, scientific progress must proceed at an accelerated rate. It must expand cumulatively, for each invention gives rise to numerous others. The capitalistic spirit which subordinates all else —or almost all else—to the maximization of profit and to money accumulation for its own sake, drives the modern production system at ever higher speed to ever greater performance—without rationally appraising the cost of the speed and the worth of the superefficiency. A purely pecuniary appraisal of speed is not an adequate appraisal; social and institutional implications must also be considered. Moreover, it is uncertain whether our pecuniary appraisal is faultless and whether the cost of obsolescence has been properly taken into account.

To sum up, civilizations resting on the modern resource pattern of inanimate energy-metal-science-capital are highly efficient as systems of physical production and therefore, theoretically at least, they are capable of freeing man from drudgery and of giving him leisure and wealth, the basis of higher spiritual development and the larger life. The system, as now developed, places a one-sided emphasis on the fund resources of inanimate energy, and therefore it cannot aspire to permanency unless that emphasis is shifted. The system, as at present constituted, lacks security and tends toward undue haste.

BIBLIOGRAPHY

Cottrell, Fred, *Energy and Society*, New York: The McGraw-Hill Book Company, Inc., 1955.

Hodgkins, Jordan A., *Soviet Power*, Englewood Cliffs, N.J.: Prentice-Hall, Inc., 1961.

Mason, Edward S., *Energy Requirements and Economic Growth*, Washington, D.C.: National Planning Association, 1955.

Power to Produce, Yearbook of Agriculture, 1960, Washington, D.C.: United States Department of Agriculture, 1960.

Schurr, Sam H., Bruce C. Netschert, Vera F. Eliasberg, Joseph Lerner, and Hans H. Landsberg, *Energy in the American Economy, 1850–1975*, Baltimore: The Johns Hopkins Press (for Resources for the Future), 1960.

Ubbelohde, A. R., *Man and Energy*, New York: George Braziller, Inc., 1955.

Wolfe, Roy I., *Transportation and Politics*, Princeton, N.J.: D. Van Nostrand Company, Inc., 1963.

World Energy Supplies, 1957–1960, Statistical Papers, Series J., No. 5, New York: Department of Economic and Social Affairs, United Nations, 1962.

6 ENERGY EXPENDITURE AND WELL-BEING

General vs. Close Correlation

That there exists a general positive correlation between energy expenditure and wealth or well-being[1] few will be inclined to question. In general, it is true that to consume more one must produce more, and production involves energy expenditure. There is something almost axiomatic about this connection between work and wealth. But to conclude from this simple logic that, because the per capita energy expenditure of one people is 20 times as great as that of another, the first people are 20 times as well off as the other, is something else again. In other words, it is one thing to concede a *general* correlation but quite a different thing to concede an *accurate* correlation. In fact, there are weighty reasons for holding that there cannot be an accurate correlation between energy expenditure and well-being. These reasons relate to some fundamental facts, not only of energy economy, but of resources in general, and are therefore developed here in some detail.[2]

Deficiencies of Statistical Treatment

Knowledge of and statistical data relating to energy sources are generally incomplete. For one thing, not all contributions of biotic energy have been accurately measured, but only those manifested through muscular energy. Thus, the appraisal of energy

---

[1] Terms such as wealth, welfare, well-being, etc., are very hard to define. So far as this analysis is concerned, any *reasonable* interpretation of these terms would appear satisfactory. One must be particularly careful not to "load" the definition with elements which favor one type of civilization as against another.

[2] See Erich W. Zimmermann, "Output of Work and Economic Well-being," *American Economic Review*, June, 1934, pp. 239–249.

sources that omits these may penalize those nations that still rely mainly on the animate energy of living organisms and are backward in the use of mechanical energy. Nations like Sweden, where much wealth is derived from the forests, and Norway, where fishing and whaling are relied on as important sources of income, may appear poorer than they actually are. In other words, the contribution to wealth and well-being made by solar radiation with or without the assistance of mechanical energy is insufficiently treated. It varies widely with both natural and cultural conditions prevailing in individual countries. Similarly, various chemical energies, especially those attributable to acids, solvents, mordants, fertilizers, explosives, etc., may be ignored. They may constitute only a minor factor in the total energy scheme, but in specific instances may noticeably affect well-being.

There just is no satisfactory statistical device for the qualitative appraisal of energy. A pound of coal is treated the same whether it is burned in an open grate with a conversion coefficient of perhaps 1 percent, or in an ultramodern gas-combustion turbine with a coefficient of possibly 25 or 30. A barrel of oil is treated alike whether it is burned as fuel oil under a boiler or converted into high-octane gasoline. A gallon of gasoline is treated alike whether it is expended in a highly efficient modern engine or a ramshackle contraption of ancient vintage. No distinction is made between the work performance of a coolie pulling a ricksha and that of a "coal miner" manipulating a 1150-ton, $750,000 excavator—or of an Edison or an Einstein for that matter. Each man is given a rating of a fraction of a horsepower reflecting the average human capacity to do physical work unaided by robots or mechanical brains. The highly skilled laborer is put on a par with "the man with the hoe." Surely, the quality of human work performance and the contribution to well-being vary sufficiently among the peoples of the earth to justify questioning the possibility of there being a close correlation between mechanically measured energy and well-being.

Obstacles to Close Correlation

Up to this point, only the adequacy of the statistical basis for testing the correlation between energy expenditure, wealth, and well-being has been questioned. Now it will be shown that, even if the most complete and perfect measurement of energy expenditure were possible, no accurate or even close correlation between energy expenditure and wealth or well-being could be expected; fundamental realities preclude such a correlation.

Chapter 1 brought out the basic fact that a sharp distinction must be made between gross resources and net resources, net resources being defined as those available for the promotion of real wealth, or well-being, after resistance had been overcome. Well-being is not directly related to gross resources, but to net resources. Nations differ widely as to the portion of their gross resources which must be devoted to overcoming resistances. Countries differ in the *configuration* or shape of their territory and that difference greatly affects the resistances, especially spatial resistances, to be overcome. Other things being equal, the ideal shape, i.e., the shape offering least resistance, is the circle. Again other things being equal, the more a country's configuration approaches the circle, the higher tends to be the ratio of net resources to gross resources, and the greater the contribution a given amount of energy makes to well-being. The shape of France is uniquely favorable, approaching that of the circle. Her overhead, especially the transportation overhead, is apt to be lower relative to work performance than that of countries whose shape is less favorable. The shape of Chile departs far from the ideal configuration. So does that of the effective portion of Canada—the narrow strip running along the international border.

This leads to another vital point: *the ratio of effective territory to total territory.* In most of western and central Europe and in the United States the two overlap. Virtually the entire national territory is occupied and forms a solid basis for the national economy. This is not the case in most other parts of the earth. Brazil is a vast mass of land, only localized areas of which are occupied. Any effort to tie these clusters into a single social economy meets with enormous resistance, causing large "energy leaks," so to speak. The same situation prevails to varying degrees in most countries of Latin America; it is perhaps even more pronounced in the Soviet Union, in most of the rest of Asia and in Africa, but probably nowhere more strikingly than in Australia.

Furthermore, countries differ greatly in *population density.* This affects the expenditures of energy required to establish the "civilizing contacts"—the means of transportation and communication. An increase in the density of population or a different geographical distribution of the population may well affect the energy requirements necessary to maintain these "contacts."

Topography is another important element affecting energy needs. If welfare were a direct and accurate function of energy expenditure, one wonders how much better off we would be if the Rocky Mountains were twice as high. Energy expenditure depends much on speed. The correlation between speed and welfare is very complex. Much speed spells a purely useless expenditure of energy. The manner in which the bulky earth materials like coal and ores, limestone, clay, etc., are distributed over the map greatly affects what may be called instrumental energy expenditure.

One of the most vital factors affecting the relationship between energy expenditure and well-being is the *age composition of the population*. Age composition affects the number of those who contribute to the social product as well as the numbers among whom this product is divided. Well-being is apt to suffer when "the cake" made by the few must be cut into too many slices.

Nations differ in their *outlook upon security* and therefore in their views regarding the diversion of effort from wealth to safety. Well-being is apt to be greatest, relative to total energy expenditure, in countries which feel most secure and hence divert a minimum of energy to the "unproductive" task of armaments and military preparedness. Similarly, homogeneous social groups in which there is relatively little tension and cause for civil strife are bound to enjoy a more favorable ratio of energy expenditure to well-being than less fortunate ones. Latin America is a region of high social tension. Her population is sharply divided into racial groups, economic classes, and social strata, a state of affairs which diverts much energy expenditure away from well-being toward sterile and obnoxious friction.

Civilizations adjust themselves to the *scarcity* no less than to the abundance *of energy*. As was brought out before, inanimate energy mobilizes; it makes people foot-loose, gives them *wanderlust*, puts them on wheels, makes them spread out, and in general encourages them to arrange their affairs on the basis of cheap and abundant energy. In the United States much energy goes to turn the wheels of our modern motor caravans. The dancing squirrel in the revolving cage also generates much energy; but where does it go? The volume of energy used is no guarantee or dependable measure of the task accomplished. Vice versa, peoples having none or only a scanty supply of inanimate energy adjust themselves to this fact by avoiding motion as much as possible. The phrase "the sedentary masses of southeast Asia" is indeed very apt. These masses are sedentary because they more or less lack the mobilizing energy of coal, oil, gas, and water power. Only by careful scrutiny of the subtle ways in which sharply contrasting civilizations operate can the relationship between energy expenditure and well-being be probed intelligently and fruitfully. Without such careful scrutiny wholly wrong conclusions are likely to be drawn from energy statistics.

The very *spirit of civilization* is affected by the amount and nature of available energy, and that spirit more than any other factor determines what energy expenditure means in terms of human well-being. In North America probably no other factor more directly affects well-being than does the spirit of freedom. As Haslam aptly remarked: "It has been said that morale is to matériel in war as three to one. In production I think spirit is to raw materials as three to one. Human energy is the keystone of the energy arch. We cannot leave it out of our logistics."[3] Indeed, "It is the spirit that quickeneth," and measurement of the spirit is something statisticians have not yet mastered.

These diverse lines of argument, far from exhausting the fullness of reality, have, it is hoped, made clear why the relationship between energy and well-being is not and cannot be a straight and simple one, but in the nature of things is bound to be highly complex. The energy rays pass through innumerable prisms before they achieve their end result—human well-being. They pass through different prisms in different lands. The net effect is influenced by the subtle forces which we like to sum up by the simple word "history." As one ponders its effects, he comes to realize the vital importance of the intangibles and the imponderables.

Energy, Exchange, and Well-Being

There remain to be discussed several specific considerations which militate against a close direct correlation between energy

[3] R. T. Haslam, in an address, "World Energy and World Peace," delivered at Massachusetts Institute of Technology Symposium on Logistics of Peace, June 12, 1948, pp. 13–14.

expenditure and well-being. The first consideration concerns the effect of exchange—trade, especially foreign trade—on the correlation here being analyzed. The varying effects of exchange on value were mentioned earlier. In a market economy the price of goods is affected not merely by the amount of work or energy that goes into making them, but also by their relative scarcity or abundance and the relative intensity of demand. It may take twice as much energy to produce an 18-million-bale cotton crop as a 9-million-bale crop, but the smaller crop under ordinary free market conditions may well sell for more than the larger crop. The extra energy put into doubling the crop may bankrupt the producers, whereas careful adjustment of supply to demand, involving the curtailment of energy expenditure, may bring great wealth. Much of the science of economics deals with this complex interaction between supply, demand, price, gross revenues, net profits, etc. Any student of the principles of economics knows that this reaction does not follow straight lines, but curves, many different curves. "The point of diminishing returns" is one of the best-known terms in all economic theory.

Energy, Capital, and Well-Being

In the modern world only a fraction of energy expenditure applies directly to the satisfaction of human wants or constitutes a direct contribution to human welfare. As was stressed before, ours is a roundabout, indirect way of producing. To satisfy hunger we do not climb a palm and cut out a coconut; we work in a hundred-million-dollar steelworks and spend our wages or salaries in stores where are sold the products of machines, hauled by railroads and motor trucks. At every point we meet capital equipment.

Capital equipment, much like culture, is the product of slow accretion. The expenditure made today may not bring a return until years later. Similarly, in a capitalistic world the well-being one enjoys today is, at least in part, the result of capital expenditures made years, perhaps decades, ago. People may coast along on the performance of their forefathers; on the other hand, they may lay the groundwork for the future well-being of generations yet unborn.

In such a world of roundabout capitalistic production where one's well-being today may result from someone else's energy expenditure ten or fifty years ago, and where one's energy expenditure today may have no effect on his own generation beyond increasing its toil and sacrifice but may contribute to the well-being of future generations,[4] statistics on energy expenditure for a single year are at least partially irrelevant to the measurement of the energy spent and the well-being enjoyed in that year. Whatever correlation exists between energy expenditure and well-being can be discovered only by the study of statistical records covering periods sufficiently long to encompass these slow processes of capital building and capital use.

Energy, International Trade, Foreign Investments, and Well-Being

Just as a single year is an inadequate unit of time for the measurement of effects of energy expenditure on well-being, so a single nation is an inadequate unit of space. Nations exchange the products of their energy expenditure in international trade. Furthermore, some nations make foreign investments, other nations receive them. One speaks of lending and borrowing nations. International loans constitute voluntary contributions made by one nation, at the expense of its own current well-being, to the current well-being of another nation in the expectation that interest and amortization will more than compensate by a future reversal of benefits. At present, the United States is sending billions of dollars' worth of goods, chiefly capital equipment, to all parts of the world; this represents a current expense to her domestic welfare but is made in the hope of future compensation, perhaps in the form of peace or of aid in war.

Moreover, in some countries much energy expenditure is made on foreign account. The oil fields of Venezuela, the Middle East, and Indonesia come to mind, as do the copper, lead, zinc, and many other mines in Latin America and Africa.

The more one follows the intricacies of modern global economy and the more realistically he pictures its manifold processes and relationships, the clearer becomes the realization that there can be no direct correlation between one year's energy expenditure in one individual nation and the state of well-being in that nation in the

---

[4] The case of the Soviet Union, engaged in enlarging and improving her capital equipment at the expense of contemporary well-being in the hope of future well-being, comes to mind.

same year. But it should be equally clear that there is no greater force promoting well-being than energy expenditure.

BIBLIOGRAPHY

Putnam, Palmer C., *Energy in the Future*, Princeton, N.J.: D. Van Nostrand Company, Inc., 1953.

Schurr, Sam H., Bruce C. Netschert, Vera F. Eliasberg, Joseph Lerner, and Hans H. Landsberg, *Energy in the American Economy, 1850–1975*, Baltimore: The Johns Hopkins Press (for Resources for the Future), 1960.

Sporn, Philip, *Energy; Its Production, Conversion, and Use in the Service of Man*, New York: The Macmillan Company, 1963.

Teitelbaum, Perry D., *Energy Production and Consumption in the United States*, Washington, D.C.: United States Department of the Interior, 1961.

7 NATURE AND RESOURCES

SOME PARADOXES OF NATURE

Nature, Friend and Foe

So great are the blessings which nature bestows upon man that he is apt to forget, at times, the hardships she brings and the terrors she holds. The deadly cobra is no less natural than the honeybee or the nightingale, the destructive hurricane no less natural than the useful trade wind, the tidal wave no less natural than the gentle rain that wets the good earth or the waterfall that drives the turbines. Nature made the fertile soil of the prairies and the plains no less than the barren, though rich, soil of the desert. Man must take the good with the bad. He strives to lessen the hard blows and make the best of the friendly help. When one thinks of natural resources, he must not forget that there are also natural resistances.

Nature, Niggardly and Bountiful

Nature appears to man as both niggardly and bountiful. She has few free gifts to offer, though these few are priceless—air to breathe, water to drink, a place to rest, friendly climate, fertile soil, game, and so forth. But free gifts of nature support only small numbers of people. As the earth's population increased and man spread from the most favored to less favored spots of natural endowment, the impression of niggardliness superseded that of bounteousness. But that was largely man's own fault. For while nature offers few free gifts to the beggar and yields little to the brute earth-robber, she proves bountiful indeed to the strong, the clever, the persevering, and the bold. Her real treasures are deeply hidden and well guarded by obstacles—i.e., resistances. Nature rewards intelligent search and wise effort with a bounty that makes her free gifts appear miserly, valuable though they are.

Nature, Constant and Changing

If nature is thought of as the universe, it may be considered constant. As was stressed earlier, nature in that sense is the topic of natural science. The social scientist is concerned not with the totality of the physical universe, but with the meaning of nature for man, with that ever-changing portion of nature which is known to man and which affects his existence. That portion is both expanding and contracting. It expands in response to increase in knowledge and improvement of the arts. Nature reveals herself ‘gradually to man, but no faster than he can learn.

The significance of this expansion may be driven home by means of the concept of *phantom resources*. Coal may be used to illustrate the meaning of that term. Let us assume that in 1900 the United States had a coal reserve of 3 trillion tons, that in that year 7 pounds of coal was necessary to generate one kilowatt-hour, and that other uses of coal were equally inefficient; that by 1950 the art of coal utilization advanced to the point where one pound of coal generates one kilowatt-hour and that other uses of coal similarly advanced in efficiency; and that during half a century the United States used up 20 billion tons of coal. Since coal is valued primarily as a source of energy and since its value as such has enhanced seven-fold, we may envisage the original 3-trillion-ton pile expanding to a phantom pile of about 20 trillion tons, an accretion which greatly overcompensates for the physical loss through use and abuse. This idea is shown pictorially in Fig. 6.

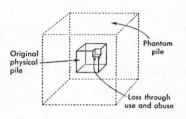

FIGURE 6. Shrinking Weight and Volume vs. Expanding Utility of Resources

This way of reasoning applies not only to fuels but to metals and other substances as well. If today a horsepower can be harnessed by means of one pound of metal, whereas a multiple was necessary fifty or a hundred years ago, here again the phantom pile appears.

These examples illustrate nature's expanding availability to man traceable to the improvement of the arts, advancing techniques, and science. The effect of discoveries can be similarly envisaged.

But nature's contributions are also subject to contraction. Minerals, especially fuels, are used up, dissipated in use. Others are rendered useless by obsolescence. Still others are damaged by man beyond repair, mainly because of ignorance, especially of the laws of ecology.

SIGNIFICANT ASPECTS OF NATURE

Distribution of the Natural Endowment

The natural materials and energies which man can utilize at the present stage of his development are largely confined to the earth itself and to that minute portion of solar radiation which reaches and is retained by the earth. The natural endowment is distributed very unevenly over this planet. First-class fertile soil is found in only a few spots, and so-called arable land makes up about 40 percent of the land surface exclusive of the polar regions. The major useful minerals are even more unevenly distributed. Climate varies widely. Topographical features add to the diversity of the picture, a diversity that applies to both resources and resistances.

The impact of this diversity of the natural endowment on man is clearly reflected in the uneven distribution of the people on the earth and in the wide differences in their economic development and living standards. While there is a close correlation between natural features and human achievements, the connection between the two is not one of direct causation, but a highly complex interaction involving many factors and forces.

Frequency of Occurrence of Resources

Not only are features of the natural environment distributed very unevenly over the earth, their distribution embodies wide variations in both amount and frequency of occurrence of resources. On the basis of frequency of occurrence, the aspects of nature may be classified as follows: (1) ubiquities (occurring everywhere, e.g., oxygen in the air); (2) commonalties (occurring in many places, e.g., tillable soil); (3) rarities[1] (occurring in few places, e.g., tin); (4) uniquities (occurring in one place, e.g., commercial cryolite).

---

[1] "Rarity" is used in preference to "scarcity" because of the meaning the latter term has in economics. Things may be very plentiful but still be scarce in the economic sense.

Frequency of occurrence is significant for several reasons. For one thing, production processes generally involve a combination of materials—for example, coal and iron. Each may occur so frequently that, by itself, it may be considered a commonalty, but usable combinations of the two may be quite rare.

Furthermore, a distinction is necessary between physical presence and availability. In a competitive price economy, for example, only the lowest-cost resource or resource combination may be used.

Another necessary distinction is between absolute and relative rarity. For example, in the absolute sense the known supply of tin is extremely limited, whereas aluminum is very common. But aluminum, in the relative sense, may be considered rare at present because current practice, determined primarily by cost of recovery and market price, exploits only rich deposits of this metal.

Finally, rarity itself varies in its effects. Rarity of a vitally important substance is of much greater concern than is rarity of a dispensable luxury. Another aspect of rarity involves the relative ease with which common substances may be substituted for rare ones. For example, the rarity of aluminum is less significant for the kitchen utensil industry than for the aircraft and electrical industries because the unusual lightness of this metal makes its use *essential* for the latter but only *desirable* for the former.

Flow and Fund Resources

The exhaustibility or permanency of resources must also be considered in connection with the frequency of their occurrence. Rarity of a resource which is self-renewable is likely to create far less serious problems than is rarity of an exhaustible resource. Thus a region may have sunshine only during relatively few periods each year, but during those periods every year the sunshine is available in undiminished amounts. A region that has small coal resources and must draw on them at the rate of 1 percent a year is in an infinitely more precarious position than a region that has water power available for its energy requirements.

Coal is a typical *fund* resource, water power a typical *flow* resource (see Fig. 3). The supply of coal is exhausted through use, whereas water power ordinarily is self-renewable. Other flow resources are monsoon winds, regularly recurring rainfall, and virgin forests (in the absence of such unfavorable forces as natural leaching, forest fires, avalanches, etc.). In general, all ecological relationships are of the flow variety, if undisturbed and subjected to no cataclysmic changes. They remain dependable resources so long as man is content with exploiting the exhaustible annual increment without interfering with the forces directing their formation. Overcutting of timber stands may affect the permanency of timber, soil, and water resources. Similarly, in many parts of the earth soil fertility under natural conditions is a self-renewable flow resource. But if depleted by continuous cultivation of plants which make heavy demands on certain of its chemicals, the soil will no longer be a self-renewable resource; it will become a wasting resource.

Not all fund resources are exhaustible; some are revolving. Most coal is burned and therefore disappears from view. Most iron, however, is used in the form of steel or cast iron and becomes a part of more or less permanent fixtures such as rails, bridges, skyscrapers, machines, etc. If protected against rust, the iron will last for many years and after use it can be scrapped and remelted and thus made available for further use. Similarly, the lead put in paint is used up; but that in batteries can be used over and over again. To the extent that reuse is possible, iron and lead and many other metals may be viewed as revolving fund resources.

"Silted" or "Choked" Flow Resources

Flow resources resemble a stream; and just as a stream can be silted up by sand, mud, and debris, so can flow resources become "silted" or "choked." The forest when properly managed can yield an endless stream of products; when put on a "sustained-yield basis" it is a flow resource. But when abused by overcutting or otherwise mismanaged, the flow of products dwindles to a mere trickle and it becomes "silted" or "choked" up. The hydrologic cycle from ocean to cloud to rain to river to ocean is one of the most important flow resources extant. Abuse and mismanagement, such as the removal of forest cover and other vegetation essential to the proper functioning of that cycle, will cause it to slow down, turn haltingly, and finally come to a stop—another example of a "silted" flow resource. Entire civilizations have been destroyed by abuse and mismanagement that allowed their vital flow resources to become silted or choked up.

However, as was pointed out in an earlier chapter, the danger of the early exhaustion of fossil fuels is being recognized and a shift from fund to flow sources of industrial energy is definitely planned. Whether man has the ingenuity to carry out this ambitious project remains to be seen. Informed persons are hopeful.

Animate and Inanimate Energy, Organic and Inorganic Matter

The division of energy into animate and inanimate was fully discussed in Chapter 4. Closely related to it is the division of matter, living and dead. So important is this division that one may refer to it as the *basic dualism of nature.*

The division into matter, living and dead, is related to, but not identical with, the division into organic and inorganic matter. Carbon is the element of life; there is no life without carbon. But, under special circumstances, carbon is preserved in the fossil fuels. Organic matter includes both living organisms and their derivatives, as well as the dead fuels.

Primary and Secondary Aspects of Nature

One may distinguish between primary or original aspects of nature, i.e., free gifts of nature, and secondary or derived aspects, i.e., aspects which become available for use by man as a result of improvements made by him—improvements in nature as well as in man himself. These improvements are called *culture.* Secondary or derived natural aspects are therefore, strictly speaking, natural-cultural resources. Nature may provide the substance or energies, but culture renders possible their use by man.

Similarly one may make a distinction between primary or original natural resistances—e.g., catastrophes such as hurricanes, earthquakes, volcanic eruptions, tidal waves, floods, etc., and disease, plant pests, poisonous plants and animals, etc.—and secondary or derived natural resistances, i.e., those that are the result of human interference with or impact on nature. The latter may be properly referred to as natural-cultural resistances.

Direct and Indirect Factors

Natural resources and resistances can be further subdivided on the basis of the directness of their relation to the processes of production and consumption. Thus one may distinguish between the resources that function directly as factors of production—such as soil, coal, wood, animals, etc.—and climate, topography, and location or conditioning factors which affect the speed and general efficiency of the production process much as a catalyst affects a chemical reaction. The same distinction can be made in the case of resistances. One may speak of direct obstacles and indirect handicaps. Moreover, both conditioning factors and indirect handicaps, like production factors and direct obstacles, can be subdivided into primary or original and secondary or derived.

LAND AND "LAND"

Changing Role of Land

The earth is divided into land and water. Land in this sense consists of the continents, the islands, and the polar regions—in short, the surface of the earth, terra firma. It is used by man chiefly in the following ways:

1. As situs, standing room, room in which to move, sites on which to build shelter, factories, villages, cities, and roads.
2. As the habitat of wild fauna and flora.
3. As the source of agricultural (including pastoral and forest) products, as soil, the premier agency for the transmutation of matter, the recipient of solar radiation and of rainfall and other climatic forces, the laboratory for photosynthesis.
4. As the source of minerals, both surface and subsoil, used in manifold ways.

For countless ages, until the coming of the power-driven machine, efforts to utilize nature were almost entirely confined to the surface of the earth. Fishing was confined to rivers, lakes, or coastal waters. Land was definitely a two-dimensional concept. Its most useful manifestation was soil, crop-bearing and animal-supporting soil.

Under these circumstances, it was natural to identify natural resources in general with land. For did not the overwhelming majority of the people engage in agriculture and therefore depend on the land, in the ordinary sense of the word, for their living? Land in the commonly accepted meaning of surface, soil, etc., was the means through which nature poured her gifts on mankind. If the climate was favorable, its effects were felt and measured in soil fertility, in the volume of crops, in the supply of feed available for herds. Likewise, the advantages of cheap water transportation, and of expanding commerce dependent thereon, were realized on the river bank and the coast—in short, on land. Thus land area, measured in acres or square miles, was an adequate indicator of man's control over natural resources in general, and it continued to be so used long after conditions had changed.

Feudalism, a system of political control and economic institutions prevailing widely during the agrarian stages of history, rested on and was built around landholding. The majority of men were mere appendages of the land, and landholding determined political power, social status, and economic well-being.

Two-Dimensional and Three-Dimensional Land

The fuller use of inanimate energy made necessary increasing drafts on subsoil mineral reserves both for fuel and for harnessing metals for useful purposes. The mechanical revolution, therefore, necessarily brought into use strata of the earth which previously had been beyond the reach of man. The subsurface was made to yield its wealth both of fossil fuels, the sources of inanimate energy itself, and of the metals required for the application and control of this new energy. Moreover, man pushed his frontiers upward as well. The air became a source of nitrogen; sunshine itself could be more fully used; radioactivity was discovered; and the energy of moving water came to be exploited in different ways and hence more fully. Generalizing, one might say that man pushed the exploitation of land vertically, both downward and upward. Land thus ceased to be identical with surface, with a thin layer of soil or surface minerals. It no longer was a two-dimensional concept; it spread out into the third dimension, to say nothing of the fourth dimension of the modern physicist. Its close identification with agriculture and animal husbandry ended. The concept came to include minerals, especially coal, petroleum, iron, copper, and similar energy and machine resources. Since minerals have gained a disproportionately great importance in relation to the areas exploited, the units of surface area have lost in value as dependable measures of the natural endowment.

Economic Terminology

This and the following two chapters are devoted to the study of the trinity of nature, man, and culture. There is a similar trilogy of terms in economic theory—land, labor, and capital.[2] While these terms, as used in traditional economic theory, correspond rather closely to nature, man, and culture as used in this analysis of resources, the two sets of terms are by no means identical. The difference stems mainly from the general approach followed in traditional economic theory and in the present analysis. Traditional economic theory, especially the part that deals with the agents of production—land, labor, capital—is primarily a short-run analysis of private enterprises or individual firms and is devoted to the study of profitable production for the market. This volume, on the other hand, is devoted mainly to the broader and long-run aspects, to the basis on which private and other enterprise rests and develops through time. Land, labor, and capital, as generally thought of, are concepts from the field of capitalistic production and private enterprise. Nature, man, and culture are as broad as the mind can encompass.

Here we are concerned primarily with the concept of land as used in economic theory. The word has to do double duty, both as land in the old two-dimensional sense and as "land" embracing all the myriad manifestations of nature acting as man's partner in the process of production. As was pointed out above, there was a time when such dual use of the word did not do violence to the basic aspects of reality. Nature functioned chiefly through land, and through land in the two-dimensional sense at that. But continued use of the word, after the realities to which it applies have changed radically, is unfortunate.

Fixity of Land and the Dynamics of Nature

The use of the word land, even in the sense of "land," is unfortunate because land in the sense of surface is something fixed, whereas "land" in the sense of the totality of nature's contribution is not fixed but highly dynamic. It never stands still. It changes constantly in response to changing human attitudes and actions and, above all, to ever-changing culture. That is the deeper meaning of

[2] A number of economists, geographers, and others now speak of *five* factors of production: land, labor, capital, the entrepreneur, and government.

the term trinity. The different factors are not wholly separate and independent, but interdependent; they act as an interdependent triple force. The land surface may be fixed, but nature as a factor in resource development is not fixed. The totality of land surface is as irrelevant to the study of the availability of resources as is the totality of matter and energy in the universe. What counts is the function and meaning of land and all other phases of nature to man.

In the absolute sense, the total supply of land on the earth may be considered fixed, limited, unalterable; but functionally appraised, "land" is alterable. There have been periods in history when the supply of land (not only in the narrow but also in the expanded sense) which was available to a given group using given methods of exploitation, was fixed, either because the group could not expand beyond its territorial boundaries or because control measures, such as social institutions or laws, artificially limited the land supply. The land available to the islander who cannot or will not move away is absolutely limited. It is not surprising to find Englishmen of the pre-steamship era worried about their limited supply of land. Feudalistic regimes tie people to the land, and the supply of land at their disposals is thereby limited.

In the Russian mir, a closed peasant community, members were held to their land by feudal laws and, in effect, were restricted in their use of land. In fact, the mir resulted from an excessive supply of land. The steppe offered a chance of escape from onerous tributes and exacting masters and from social restrictions in general. The mir meant the closing of that avenue of escape. Similarly, our own "frontier," especially the open spaces of the West, beckoned to settlers unsatisfied with conditions in the East. Slavery in the South was in part a defensive measure against the effects of the "frontier" on the labor market. The virtual absence of restrictions on westward migrations since the Civil War has left its indelible imprint on the very soul of this country. Thus it is apparent that the supply of land must be interpreted relatively to time and place.

CULTIVABILITY

Importance of Cultivable Land

Regardless of the rise of machine industry and the corresponding relative decline of agriculture, the problem of food supply and the question of limits of cultivable land remain crucial. As will be shown in the next chapter, the population of the earth is increasing rapidly and in some parts in an explosive fashion. The problem of providing sustenance for a greatly increased human family is serious. How much cultivable land exists is therefore a crucial question facing man.

Limitations of Cultivability

As has been stated repeatedly, nature sets outer limits to man's potential resources, but within these outer limits there lies a broad and sunny land where human initiative, drive, and ingenuity are given wide play. This applies to cultivable land as to all natural phenomena. The physical limitations, the outer limits, will be taken up first.

The total land area of the earth is estimated to be somewhere between 57 and 58 million square miles, or approximately 37 billion acres. Of this, almost 6 million square miles lie in the polar regions. Of the remaining 52 million square miles, about one-fourth is in grassland, about one-third in desert, and about two-fifths in forest. Agricultural experts agree that about 40 percent of the total land area outside of the arctic regions, or about 21 million square miles, may be considered arable. In any attempt to ascertain the total land area available for agriculture, a sharp distinction between two sets of limiting conditions should be made—one absolute, the other relative. Obviously there is some land which, under no circumstances at present worthy of consideration,[3] can be made to produce anything. Scattered savages or nomads can eke out an existence on some land by gathering the plant or animal products that nature freely yields. But agriculture implies a settled population and can therefore be carried on only if the yield is sufficient to justify more or less permanent settlement and thereby to support a settled population. Some agricultural regions reward man's effort moderately, while others yield bountifully. Thus appraised by absolute standards of natural productivity, the land surface of the earth appears like a crazy quilt made up of many-colored patches of different

---

[3] "Circumstances at present worthy of consideration" are here understood to embrace such developments of the arts, of population trend, of standards of living, and of other pertinent factors as may reasonably be assumed to lie within the range of prophecy, the calculation being confined to a period of time clearly within the range of present economic, social, and political consideration.

materials, some rich green, some gray, others bleached white, some of rich texture, others threadbare.

The determination of the general cultivability of the earth, especially as reflected in the physical limits of food production, is of vital importance, for without food human life cannot exist. Hence, the limits of food production set the limits of all production. In the light of what has been said, this question of the physical limits of world food supply is considered rather theoretical. It is safe to assume that in the calculable future the world's food supply will depend primarily on the development of the arts, especially on increased knowledge of agronomy, plant and animal breeding, biology, the increasingly available and efficient use of capital equipment, and, above all, on the fuller utilization of inanimate energy. But it will also depend upon improved knowledge of dietetics and the prevailing attitude toward food consumption. For the calculable future, therefore, the question of the physical limits of cultivability will remain purely academic. Furthermore, in view of present population trends, which are discussed later, and in view of the rate of progress made in the technological arts, it seems doubtful whether the worst areas of the earth will at any foreseeable future date have to be put under the plow or otherwise made to yield their products to man.

In ascertaining the absolute limits of cultivability or physical productivity, four factors are generally distinguished:[4]

1. Temperature conditions, particularly growing-season temperatures and dates of occurrence of spring and fall frosts.
2. Moisture conditions; i.e., rainfall, snowfall, hail, fog, humidity, rate of evaporation.
3. Topography, or land form; i.e., the configuration of the earth's surface, degree and direction of slope, roughness or smoothness of the land.
4. Soils, including both physical structure and chemical and bacteriological characteristics.

These limiting factors are sometimes spoken of as the four physical frontiers of agriculture. The determination of these frontiers is the major task of the geographer, especially the climatologist, or the soil expert.

[4] O. E. Baker, "The Potential Supply of Wheat," *Economic Geography*, March, 1925, p. 21.

One example must suffice here to illustrate the governing principles. (See Fig. 7.) In view of its importance as the staff of life, wheat is chosen for this purpose:

> Only one acre in ten of the land of the world is physically available for wheat production. Adverse climatic conditions prevent production on nearly four-fifths of the land, and of that climatically available, about 11 million square miles, over one-third is too hilly

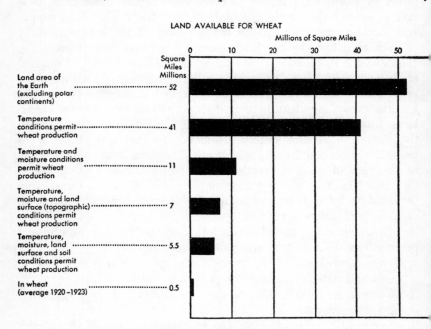

FIGURE 7. Land Available for Wheat

or rough for wheat cultivation, reducing the area to 7 million square miles. Unfavorable soils still further reduce by a fifth the area climatically and topographically available, leaving only 5½ million square miles physically suitable for wheat. But this tenth of the land surface physically available exceeds present requirements, less than one acre in ten of this available land being utilized for wheat. In other words, less than one per cent of the land surface of the earth is in wheat at present. Since corn, oats, hay, vegetables and other crops must also be grown on land suitable for wheat, it appears unlikely that over three per cent of the world's land surface will ever be devoted to wheat production.[5]

It would be a grave error to apply the findings regarding wheat or any other selected crop to the determination of the general cultivability of the earth's surface. For one thing, crops compete with one another and with pasture lands and forests. They compete with cities, highways, and industrial uses for some of the best land and usually give way to the economic rewards inherent in these other uses. Furthermore, the relation of minerals to agricultural production must be kept in mind. The competition between a field of fodder corn or a section of pasture and coal or petroleum is as real as that between wheat and corn in parts of the U.S. Corn Belt. The tractor competes with the horse and the mule, animate energy with inanimate, living matter with dead substance.

Cultural and Human Limitations of Cultivability

As noted above, nature sets the outer limits. Culture and human attitudes and actions determine the range of actual use within these outer limits. Cultures differ chiefly in their command over energy. The impact of culture on the cultivability of land, therefore, can best be demonstrated by comparing the cultivation of land under two civilizations which differ sharply in the extent of their command over energy. These civilizations are China, historically a sedentary vegetable civilization, and the United States, a highly mobilized machine civilization.

Land cultivation in China as compared with that in the United States constitutes a strange paradox. Unfortunately, accurate data are not available; at this time, the definition of China is still being debated between East and West. The area of China (including Tibet and Sinkiang) is approximately 3.7 million square miles and that of the United States (including Alaska and Hawaii) about 3.6 million square miles. China's population is estimated to be approximately 700 million; that of the United States about 190 million. The population density of China is about 190 per square mile compared with 53 in the United States. The population density of China is over 3.7 times that of the United States, based upon total land

[5] This quotation and Fig. 7 are from *ibid.*, p. 31.

area; it is almost 4.5 times that of the United States if based on estimated areas considered *physically* cultivable.[6] Under these conditions, one would most certainly expect the Chinese to cultivate a far greater percentage of their total land area and a still greater portion of their smaller physically cultivable land. But, paradoxically, the very opposite is the case.

The paradox becomes even more striking in view of the fact that about three-fourths of the Chinese working population, or upwards of 525 million people, normally engage in cultivating the land whereas only about 10 percent of the working population of the United States cultivates an acreage half again as large.

Inanimate Energy and Cultivability

The explanation of all these paradoxical statements is perfectly simple—*energy;* more specifically, the historic absence of inanimate energy in Chinese agriculture, and its prodigal use in American agriculture. This difference in energy use affects not only agriculture directly, but the entire system of production and consumption—in fact, the entire civilization.

In China, agriculture virtually amounts to food production for local consumption. The farms must first of all support the workers that till the field. In China, agriculture is its own powerhouse. It provides the fuel (food) for the engines (labor) of production. In China, the laborer is little supported by tools or animals, and less by machine power. In China, agriculture must also support the families of the workers, those in government service, the army, etc., and finally, the landlords.

Chinese agriculture exhausts itself by trying to provide the energy needed to work the fields. Little energy is left to supply locomotion, i.e., movement from place to place. Such movement is an unattainable luxury; hence China's sedentary character; hence, the traditional division into thousands of local self-sufficient *hsiens;* hence, the incredible crowding on the cream of the land. Land that yields all the energy that is needed for its own cultivation must be wonderful land. What is more, it must be cultivated in a wonderfully intensive fashion. Fertilizer must be piled on it, water must be

---

[6] The reader is reminded that these figures are gross approximations. However, the contrasts are so sharp that no reasonable correction of statistical data could be expected to affect appreciably the main points brought out here.

supplied in prodigious amounts, labor, care, and skill must be showered on every square foot, or else the equation will not balance and somebody will starve.

Human labor is incredibly slow. Baker estimated that it takes one man fifteen days to spade an acre,[7] and correspondingly long to harvest. That cuts two good slices of precious time from the length of the campaign. It shortens the growing and ripening season and thus cuts down the choice of crops. Only crops which fit this rigorous timetable and have high yields will be tolerated.

The Chinese farmer performs miracles in yield *per acre* but, in spite of truly pathetic efforts and admirable skill in which is embodied the wisdom of forty centuries, he accomplishes pitifully little in terms of *per capita* yield. The American farmer, in general, lags behind in yield per acre but performs miracles in yield per capita. The chief reason is the latter's prodigal use of outside energy, chiefly inanimate energy. *Inanimate energy mobilizes.* It permits one farmer to cultivate hundreds, even thousands of acres. The tractor and the combine go far to explain the American agricultural marathon. Each farmer is aided by numerous robots, obedient slaves that never eat. Nearly every pound of rice that comes out of monsoon Asia was produced with human energy that was fueled by rice or other food. Most of the energy, other than solar radiation, that produces wheat on our prairies and plains was produced with the aid of coal, oil, and electricity.

Not only is each American farmer aided by robots working beside him, numerous workers in factories, similarly aided by other robots, stand behind him, furnishing the machines and vehicles and structures that make a factory of a sort out of the modern farm. Behind the farmer stands also one of the greatest research organizations of all time, the United States Department of Agriculture, and the various state organizations and numerous county agents who incorporate in their collective knowledge the fruit of decades of systematic research, one of the brightest achievements of machine civilization. This scientific research goes far to enable the American farmer to do surprisingly well even in terms of yield per acre.

While man power is painfully slow, machine power is astonishingly fast. Artificial light turns night into day; and hence, in twenty-

[7] O. E. Baker, "Agriculture and the Future of China," *Foreign Affairs*, April, 1928.

four hours, with the aid of tractors a farmer and a few helpers can cultivate and harvest areas of land which thousands of men could hardly cultivate and harvest in weeks. The effect in terms of lengthened growing and ripening seasons is stupendous. The choice of crops widens by leaps and bounds. Crop cultivation can be extended to colder regions.

The most dramatic effect of the use of inanimate energy in farming, besides the prodigious yield per man, is the extension of farming into regions whose counterparts in China must lie unused because of their poor quality. A vital law of cultivation reads: the fertility of cultivable land is in inverse proportion to the amount of energy supporting the cultivator. Assuming reasonable prices, a farmer cultivating over a thousand acres with tractors and combines can make a profit on perhaps 12 bushels of wheat per acre, whereas a robotless peasant, cultivating a fraction of the land, may have to get 30 bushels to break even.

The machine, in other words, breaks the critical link between food and work that is the crux of Chinese agriculture. In doing so it vastly enlarges the cultivability of land. It explains why American farmers, satisfied with relatively low yields of many basic crops, nevertheless can feed themselves and their families well, can feed the rest of the nation, and can make remarkable contributions to the rest of the world.

Cultivability in an Exchange Economy

The peasant produces primarily for himself and his household. The American farmer produces to sell. Prices of the things he sells and of the things he buys thus become a vital factor in the determination of cultivability. Prices, in turn, must be related to costs, not only costs of production but also delivery costs. Accessibility to the market and to sources of supply becomes as important as fertility itself. The law governing the relationship of energy to fertility, stated above, applies to accessibility as well. Costs, in turn, reflect not only wage rates and prices of purchased goods, interest rates, taxes, etc., but also skill, quality of management, application of service, etc. In short, in an exchange economy cultivability becomes a function of numerous factors associated with many phases of culture.

The problem of determining the cultivability of land has been developed fully, not merely for its own sake, but also to illustrate the overall problem for man, of the availability of aspects of nature. The main lesson to be learned is that availability in general, as well as cultivability in particular, is not determined once and for all and for all peoples alike. Availability no less than cultivability varies with time and place, is a reflection of the culture pattern of each age and people. A key to availability in general and to cultivability in particular is the use made of energy—more specifically, inanimate energy.

BIBLIOGRAPHY

A Place to Live, Yearbook of Agriculture, 1963, Washington, D.C.: United States Department of Agriculture, 1963.

Clawson, Marion, R. Burnell Held, and Charles H. Stoddard, *Land for the Future,* Baltimore: The Johns Hopkins Press (for Resources for the Future), 1960.

Demographic and Economic Change in Developed Countries, National Bureau of Economic Research, Princeton: Princeton University Press, 1960.

Higbee, Edward, *American Agriculture: Geography, Resources, Conservation,* New York: John Wiley & Sons, Inc., 1958.

Lord, Russell, *The Care of the Earth,* New York: Thomas Nelson & Sons, 1962.

Myrdal, Gunnar, *Rich Lands and Poor,* New York: Harper & Row, Publishers, Inc., 1957.

Population and Food Supply (No. 7), *Possibilities of Increasing World Food Production* (No. 10), and *Third World Food Survey* (No. 11) from a 16-part series *Freedom From Hunger Campaign,* Rome, Italy: Food and Agriculture Organization, United Nations, 1962 and 1963.

Schultz, Theodore W., *The Economic Organization of Agriculture,* New York: The McGraw-Hill Book Company, Inc., 1953.

8 MAN AND RESOURCES

DUAL ROLE OF MAN

Man is both the most dynamic agent of production and the beneficiary of the entire process of resource development and utilization. As was pointed out in Chapter 1, resources are instrumental wealth which, after helping to overcome resistances, yield real wealth—the well-being of man. As an agent of production man contributes his labor, mental and physical; with the aid, "advice, and consent" of nature he builds culture to make his production efforts more effective and to lessen the impact of resistances; he discovers new ways and invents new arts; his aspirations furnish aim and purpose. As beneficiary he enjoys the advantages of advancing civilization.

One must not think of the two roles as separate in time and place. Happiness may be found in the joy of achievement and in the pride of workmanship. The greatest advances in civilization are made through the improvement of man's role as an agent of production. The greatest contribution to real wealth lies in that improvement. As was stated earlier, man is predestined to be the director, planner, and aspirer. As his role shifts from that of the toiling field hand or sweating ditch digger to that of master of robots and director of inanimate forces, he reaps the fruit of real wealth to which he seems predestined by his unique aptitudes. Since this is the acme of resource strategy and functional specialization, the productivity of the entire process of resource development is raised; and besides finding "real wealth" in the performance of his role as an agent of production, man reaps a richer harvest of material goods and greater leisure.

It is the recognition of these fundamental truths that gives the processes of mechanization and industrialization significance far beyond their immediate effects on increased productivity and enlarged profits.

To be able to perform this higher role, man must be physically fit and healthy, and properly educated and trained. The promotion of public health and education thus assumes an importance that can hardly be exaggerated. Human resources are both the most dynamic and the most potent; they are also the most precious because, to repeat, they combine the task of production agent with the end object of the entire process. They constitute the *end values to be achieved* in the process.

MAN-LAND RATIO AND POPULATION DENSITY

Definition of Terms

What roles human beings are allowed to play depends largely on a highly significant ratio sometimes referred to as the *man-land ratio*. In all the social sciences there is no more fundamental relationship than that between man and land: "The ultimate elements offered for a scientific study of the evolution and life of human society are Man and Land; given these, there arises at once the necessity of adjustment between them. How much land there is to how many men is the fundamental consideration in the life of any society."[1]

The concept land must be interpreted in the broadest sense of natural opportunities as affected by the state of cultural development. Under no circumstances must the man-land ratio be confused with population density. The latter concept is a purely mechanical one referring to a simple *quantitative* relationship between numbers of people and numbers of units of land area—acres, hectares, square miles, etc. Population density figures are particularly meaningless when applied to large areas such as China, Canada, Brazil, the Soviet Union. The overall density figure is on the average as meaningless as would be the amount 4 inches for the average height of vegetation in Mozambique. The overall population density figure for Egypt is meaningless because Egypt is divided into the incredibly overcrowded Nile valley and the virtually empty desert spaces on both sides of that river. Brazil, as was mentioned before, is a huge area over which there are scattered clusters of human habitation, with the bulk of the people living on mere fractions of the total area. Canada's population is crowded into the strip paralleling the

[1] W. G. Sumner and A. G. Keller, *The Science of Society*, Yale University Press, New Haven, 1927, vol. 1, p. 4.

international boundary; the rest of her vast territory is virtually uninhabited.

The man-land ratio is a highly complex concept of a *qualitative* relationship. Statistical data of population density per square mile are of little value to the social scientist except as a starting point. There are densely populated areas where people live in squalor and poverty; there are others whose standards of living are high. Vice versa, there are sparsely populated areas whose inhabitants barely eke out an existence; in others they live in comfort if not in wealth. The man-land ratio takes into account all the human qualities bearing on productivity and all the environmental aspects, both natural and cultural, affecting the availability of resources. A high population density figure may indicate overpopulation; but even a region with a low population density may be overpopulated. Only the qualitative and critical appraisal of human wants and abilities and of the availability of resources can furnish conclusive evidence as to the true state of affairs.

Internal and External Carrying Capacity

To determine the man-land ratio, land must not be measured simply in square miles, but evaluated as to its carrying capacity, i.e., the capacity to support human life, to satisfy human wants. In primitive closed societies whose arts and standards of living are static, this carrying capacity can be easily appraised; but advancing civilization, with its growing complexity of social organization, with its progress in arts and sciences, with the increasing importance of commerce, renders this measurement difficult. When nature largely determines productivity, as was the case in primitive times, acres or square miles indicate the carrying capacity, at least under like or similar conditions. Today the wealth of subsoil minerals invests acres with a carrying capacity which formerly did not exist. The arts and institutions become more and more important as factors determining capacity. Above all, by causing the breakdown of self-sufficiency, commerce and finance create a spatial gap between place of production and place of consumption. Carrying capacity must therefore be redefined in the light of changed conditions. To the original idea of internal carrying capacity must be added the so-called external capacity.

A self-sufficient farm or a self-sufficient manor depends physically on the land, its own internal carrying capacity. A mining camp or a village craftsman, on the other hand, depends on exchange for sustenance. They exchange the products of their own land and labor for those of other men and places. They place commercial dependence on external carrying capacity. Similarly, self-sufficient nations and commercial nations may be differentiated. Great Britain may exchange coal for wheat; we may prefer to live on the produce of our own fields and mines. Great Britain may have invested savings in foreign lands, collecting the interest in foodstuffs and raw materials. Legal claims, established by conquest or trade, on land hundreds or thousands of miles away have become important features of modern economy. Thus, the direct relationship between the number of people and the number of square miles on which they live has lost much of its meaning and with it has gone some of the meaning of population density figures.

A region nowadays must be considered overpopulated only if the internal and external capacity on which it can draw for its support is inadequate. It is estimated that the physical internal carrying capacity of the Netherlands is sufficient to support 120 people to the square mile—the actual density in that country is around 900 per square mile. But nobody who knows economic conditions in that prosperous trading country would consider the Netherlands overpopulated. Its carrying capacity includes other parts of the earth on which, because of political, commercial, and financial influence, it can draw for support. While it draws on these areas for support it also contributes to their carrying capacity.

Pent-Up and Expanding Populations

Not all peoples are in a position to draw upon external carrying capacity, either economically or politically. Moreover, nations differ widely in the extent to which they can enlarge their economic support by drawing on other parts of the world. The extent to which Great Britain was able to do so for centuries is a unique experience of human history. After the defeat of her naval rivals Portugal, Spain, Denmark, the Netherlands, and France, she had virtually the entire globe at her feet. Later on, when France, the Netherlands, and Belgium became linked to Britain in common opposition to German expansion, they too were allowed to share in overseas colonies, to hold what they had and to acquire new ones.

One point regarding colonies which is apt to be overlooked should be made clear. There is such a thing as colonial exploitation. Slave raids and the sacking of rich cities such as the capitals of Montezuma and the Inca definitely fall in that category, as does the ruthless treatment of the rubber gatherers in both the Amazon basin and the Congo. But one must not lose sight of the fact that much colonial enterprise definitely comes under the heading of conversion of "neutral stuff" into resources. The colonizer creates many of the resources which he takes out and in many instances he contributes to the welfare of the native population.

The history of the United States is virtually the history of expansion, first over the continental homeland, and then overseas. Similarly, the history of Russia was the history of eastward expansion to the Pacific and beyond, to which World War II added westward expansion to the Adriatic and halfway into Germany. Brazil may belong in this category, with her expansion still to come.

Fig. 8[2] is here reproduced not merely to focus attention on

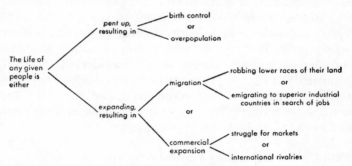

FIGURE 8. Pent-up and Expanding Peoples

important relationships between population pressure and economic, social and political phenomena but also to arouse critical thinking on the specific ideas suggested by the figure.

One point that deserves to be questioned in particular concerns the connection between the state of being pent-up and birth control. Birth control, as will be brought out more fully later on, ordinarily indicates a high level of economic productivity which can hardly

[2] T. N. Carver, "Some Needed Refinements of the Theory of Population," in M. Sanger, *Proceedings of the World Population Conference,* Edward Arnold & Co., London, 1927, p. 124.

be associated with the idea of being pent-up. The frontiers of science and technology are as real as geographical frontiers; and no people are truly pent-up that add billions of robots to their supporting staff and in general push back the frontiers of human knowledge and enlarge their capacity to tap the powers and riches of nature.

Sometimes people have felt pent-up when perhaps they were not. Even an illusory sense of being pent-up may affect human attitudes sufficiently to bring repercussions on group behavior.

WORLD POPULATION MAP

Major Centers

A glance at a map showing the distribution of population will reveal three outstanding centers of population concentration:
1. Eastern and Southeast Asia, especially China, India, Japan, Korea, but also including Java.
2. The industrialized areas of western, northern, and central Europe, especially Belgium, the Netherlands, Great Britain, and Germany, but also including other areas such as northern Italy, the Barcelona sector of Spain, parts of France, and Czechoslovakia.
3. The industrial areas of the United States.

The three population centers listed above differ widely in historical background and economic support. Hundreds of millions of people are massed in the coastal plains and river valleys of southeastern Asia. In Europe and in the northeastern United States, the great concentration centers lie over or near the coal fields; more recently, water power, petroleum, and natural gas have also proved strong drawing cards. Everywhere large numbers flock to the crossroads of commerce. Huntington[3] points out that the Asiatic centers lie in the monsoon belts, the areas of abundant food (per acre), and the centers of Europe and North America in the cyclonic storm belts, the areas of abundant energy. He refers to human energy in this connection; but, in general, these sections are also the areas of abundant mechanical energy where millions of horsepower are installed and billions of kilowatt-hours are generated from coal and other fossil fuels.

These three centers vary widely in the number of people they

[3] See E. Huntington, *The Human Habitat,* D. Van Nostrand Company, Inc., New York, 1927, especially chap. 2.

support, in economic status, and in political power. Roughly, the magnitudes of the three centers, in the order listed above, may be indicated by the figures 1.7 billion, 400 million, 180 million approximate population; or 8.5, 2, and 1, showing the ratio of the population figures. Together, these three centers account for about three-fourths the total population of the earth.

As is well known, these three population centers represent sharply differentiated types of civilization. In particular, the cleavage between the oriental vegetable civilization of monsoon Asia and the machine civilization of the West is very wide. The difference between Europe and North America is largely one of degree, but the difference between the East and the West is one of kind. As was shown in Chapter 5, the difference is traceable largely to the use of inanimate energy or the failure to use it. A good way to explain economic status and political power is in terms of men *and* robots. In this connection it should be realized that vegetable civilizations may be definitely overpopulated and therefore suffer from excess of numbers. As yet there is no sign of permanent overpopulation of robots, though in times of depression some observers suspect temporary overcrowding and advocate birth control for machines.

Population Distribution and Agricultural Production

The map shown in Fig. 9 suggests a significant correlation between the distribution of people and agricultural land use. It is a natural correlation, one to be expected in view of the dependence of human life and work energy on food, the chief product of agriculture. By and large, people live where they can obtain their food, or, vice versa, agriculture flourishes where there are people to cultivate the land, or near the great urban centers.

If tiny global maps like Fig. 9 were blown up to many times their size and compared to others showing world population distribution, one would quickly discover that the overlapping of human populations and agricultural activity, while almost literally true in monsoon Asia, is not quite as complete as these small maps seem to suggest. The more inanimate energy is used, the larger the number of robots per capita of human population, and the less close the detailed local overlapping. Western Germany used to draw food

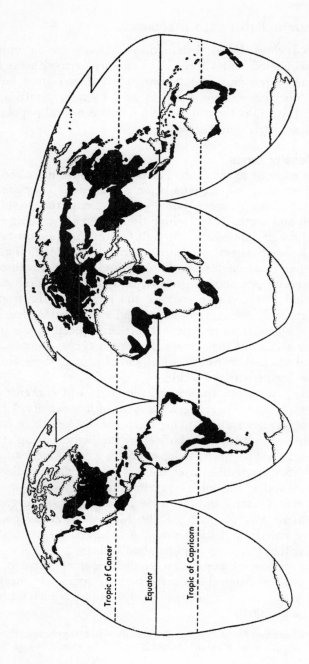

FIGURE 9. World Areas of Arable Agriculture

from eastern regions. Great Britain draws heavily on the outside world. In the United States there are vast surplus food areas that supply the needs not only of her own industrialized areas but of Europe and other parts of the world as well. Even in countries like Argentina and Australia there is a division between local population centers and local agricultural areas.

Other Density Zones

In sharp contrast to the centers of population just discussed are the empty spots on a map of population distribution. They are the great arid or semiarid zones lying mainly along the twentieth parallel north and south. They include the vast area stretching from the Sahara through Asia Minor, through Central Asia almost to the Pacific, the Kalahari Desert of South Africa, most of Australia, the dry region that cuts across South America from Peru through Bolivia down into southern Argentina, and the dry zones of the western United States. There are also the regions of the tropical rainforest, especially the Amazon basin and equatorial Africa. The habitability of the African continent is further reduced by the prevalence of the tsetse fly that causes sleeping sickness in men and similarly fatal diseases in cattle. And then, of course, there are the polar regions, both north and south.

Between these empty spaces and the centers of concentration are various gradations. There are wide areas of low density, 1 to 15 inhabitants per square mile. "Among them are some of the colonies of recent European settlement which enjoy the highest living standards in the world. The western slopes of the North American continent, the Canadian prairies and the uplands of the middle-west of the United States, the inland grazing areas of South America, the drier regions of central and east Africa, coastal Arabia, the greater part of southern Siberia, parts of the Malayan archipelago, the coastal rim of eastern and southeastern Australia and most of New Zealand, lie within this zone of population density."[4]

The low density of population in these regions is partly due to more or less unchangeable causes such as sparse or uncertain rainfall. But in part it is due to social conditions and human attitudes which may be changed.

[4] See J. B. Condliffe, *The Economic Pattern of World Population*, Planning Pamphlet No. 18, National Planning Association, Washington, 1943, p. 8.

Some regions, such as the Matto Grosso of Brazil, are as yet inadequately opened up; they await the spur of foreign investments in the form of modern means of transportation, machinery, scientific methods, etc. Other regions are deliberately closed to those most eager to come—people from overworked, underdeveloped areas of Asia and Europe. The present settlers, lucky to have come first, enjoy an enviable living standard and seek to perpetuate it by political measures. This applies particularly to New Zealand and Australia, but also to the United States and parts of Latin America.

The carrying capacity of some of these regions may have been permanently reduced by predatory farming, widespread destruction of forests, and general impairment of soil fertility and sound ecological relationships. In places the situation has been aggravated by pests, native and imported.[5] As Condliffe points out, many of these areas were merely *staked out* rather than occupied; now the defense of the stakes precludes real occupation.

The next zone of density is that having a population density of 15 to 75 inhabitants per square mile. It includes two very distinct types of settlement. The first is exemplified by the older settlements in Europe, Africa, and Asia; the second, by settlements in the New World. The type distinction derives both from the quality of the land and from the cultural levels of the inhabitants.

Even in this zone of density one becomes aware of the contrast between the western European type of capitalist, mechanized farming supported by and leading naturally to urban aggregation and the Asiatic peasant type of farming, which is decentralized, more dependent upon human labor, less equipped with power and yielding much lower standards of living. This distinction must obviously be borne in mind when grouping in one zone of density the highly-developed farming regions of the middle-western American states and the poor uplands of China. The distinction is vital, perhaps the most vital of the whole problem of world population. It is a contrast between areas in which unrestrained pressure of numbers upon limited resources is kept in check only by the harsh forces of nature and those in which human control over natural conditions (especially over sources of physical energy) and not less over social organization, has enabled numbers to expand while raising living standards. On the one hand we find low levels of human livelihood, scientific

[5] Good examples are the kangaroo and rabbit, respectively, in Australia. See *ibid.*, p. 9.

ignorance, social anarchy, and natural controls over population increase—on the other, high levels of achievement, increasing scientific knowledge and conscious human control of numbers by limitation of births.[6]

This contrast may be followed all the way up to the most densely populated areas. In fact, the contrast becomes sharper as population density increases until finally it reaches its extremes in such contrasts as Pittsburgh and the Yangtze valley or London and the Nile valley.

POPULATION STATISTICS

Size of World Population

How many people live on the earth is not known. In countries whose aggregate population constitutes between two-thirds and three-fourths of the total population of the earth, periodical counts are taken more or less regularly, but even then a margin of error of probably 10 percent must be conceded. This margin of error is small compared to that which affects estimates of the rest of the world's population. Taking into consideration the margin of error, the total world population was estimated by the United Nations to be just over 3 billion in 1960.

Growth of World Population

While, as was stated above, nowadays one-fourth to one-third of the population of the world is not covered by official census records, this was true of about four-fifths of the world's population in 1800. Therefore, any attempt to reconstruct the past growth of the world's population is highly precarious, for one must rely on inference and on logic. Those well versed in the intricacies of vital statistics, actuarial science, and demography can use these delicate instruments with reasonable assurance. Fortunately, some outstanding statisticians have devoted themselves to this study. The composite results of numerous studies are summarized in Fig. 10. The comments following the graph are taken from Notestein.[7]

---

[6] *Ibid.*, pp. 10–11.
[7] See Frank W. Notestein, "Population—The Long View," a chapter in Theodore W. Schultz (ed.), *Food for the World*, University of Chicago Press, Chicago, 1945, pp. 36–57. Fig. 10 is reprinted by permission from *ibid.*

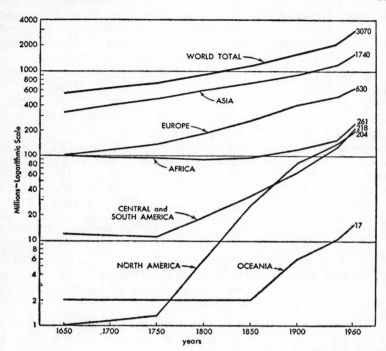

FIGURE 10. Growth of World Population by Continents, 1650–1960

The figure brings out three facts pertinent to this discussion.

1. The world's population has been growing at a rapid and accelerating pace during the last three centuries. Since the middle of the seventeenth century it has grown at an average annual rate of about 5 per thousand. Since 1900 the annual increase has averaged 8 per thousand. Such prolonged and rapid increase cannot have occurred frequently in the history of the race; and, obviously, increases of this magnitude have never occurred before. For example, if the average rate of increase obtaining since 1650 had been in force since the beginning of the Christian Era, an initial population of only 10 million would now amount to more than fifty times the present world population. The modern epoch of growth has been unique.

2. All sections of the world have participated in this growth, but it has been particularly marked in Europe and Europe overseas, especially prior to 1900.

TABLE 2.   Estimated Population of the World, 1650–1960[a] (in millions)

Continent	1650	1750	1800	1850	1900	1960
Europe	100	140.0	187.0	266	401	630
North America	1	1.3	5.7	26	81	204
Central and South America	12	11.1	18.9	33	63	218
Oceania	2	2.0	2.0	2	6	17
Africa	100	95.0	90.0	95	120	261
Asia	330	479.0	602.0	749	937	1740
Total	545	728.4	905.6	1171	1608	3070

[a] 1650–1900, estimates by Willcox, revised by Carr-Saunders; 1960 figures modified from United Nations, *Demographic Yearbook*.

3. Since 1900 the rate of growth has tended to decline in Europe, North America, and Oceania; but in Africa, Asia, and Central and South America there apparently has been some acceleration of the rate of increase.

The main facts shown by this graph may be appreciated more readily when supported by statistical evidence, such as that in Table 2.

The accelerated rate of growth of world population is evident in the following figures showing increases for the periods indicated:

1651–1750, 33.6 percent
1751–1850, 60.8 percent
1851–1960, 162.1 percent

Prospects of Future Population Growth

The prediction of population growth is impossible, for no one can predict the events which will affect that growth; in particular, realistic predictions of migration are impossible. Even a rough estimate of how many people will be living on this planet in the year 2000 is a wild gamble, a purely hypothetical procedure. Proof of this is that estimates made in the mid-1960s vary between 6 to 7 billion total world population for the year 2000 if present rates are maintained. Statisticians have worked out ingenious methods of calculating prospective growth as determined by the orderly projection of known past trends. Such prognoses are ". . . illustrative of the underlying and orderly processes of population change."[8]

DEMOGRAPHY

It was pointed out in the preceding section that the prediction of future population growth is impossible but that expectation of future trends may be based on past trends. In order to be able to do this intelligently, one must know what figures mean, what forces are at work to bring about certain results; in short, he must be versed in the science of population, demography. Here only a few elementary concepts of demography are discussed briefly as an aid to the discussion of population history which follows.

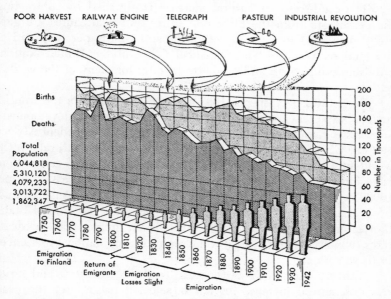

FIGURE 11. The Universal Cycle of Population Growth Under the Industrial Revolution, as Experienced by Sweden

[8] Frank W. Notestein, Irene B. Taueber, Dudley Kirk, Ansley J. Coale, and Louise K. Kiser, *The Future Population of Europe and the Soviet Union*, League of Nations, Geneva, 1944, p. 21.

Factors Involved

Putting a highly complex process into simple lay language, one may say that births and immigration affect population growth positively, whereas deaths and emigration affect it negatively. For an illustration of these four elements of population growth, see Fig. 11. The actual rate of growth of a given population depends on birth rates, death rates, and the relative volume of immigration and emigration. These elementary factors, in turn, are affected by age and sex composition and by a myriad of factors that make up the historical setting and environmental background of the group, including events such as natural catastrophes, wars, depressions, etc.

Crude Birth and Death Rates, and Crude Rates of Natural Increase

The crude rate of natural increase is obtained by subtracting the death rate from the birth rate. Birth and death rates are generally expressed in numbers of births and deaths per thousand of the total population.[9] The Statistical Office of the United Nations publishes crude birth and crude death rates for many of the world's nations.

Birth rates over 40 per 1000 are not uncommon in the frontier regions experiencing rapid political and economic development. Such rates characterize a number of the newly independent African nations; Ghana, for example, had the highest crude birth rate in the world in 1960 with 55.8 per 1000.[10] Most Latin American nations have birth rates over 30 per 1000 and many are in excess of 40 per 1000. In general, birth rates in the African and Latin American nations exceed those of northwestern Europe and the United States by two or three times. The birth rates are far greater than the death rates, which explains the large increases in population experienced in these nations.

Table 3 lists crude birth rates, crude death rates, and crude rates of natural increase for a few selected nations for the years 1937 and 1960.

[9] A more sophisticated rate is the ratio of girl babies born per 100 (or 1000) of women of child-bearing age.

[10] This reference does not include many small political units nor any political unit for which data were provisional.

TABLE 3. Crude Birth Rates, Crude Death Rates, and Crude Rates of Natural Increase per 1000 for Selected Countries, 1937 and 1960[a]

	1937	1960		1937	1960
Austria	12.8	17.8	Rumania	30.8	19.1
	—13.3	—12.7		—19.3	— 8.7
	— 0.5	5.1		11.5	10.4
Belgium	15.4	16.9	Spain	22.7	21.9
	—13.2	—12.9		—19.0	— 8.7
	2.2	4.0		3.7	13.2
Czechoslovakia	16.2	15.9	Sweden	14.4	13.7
	—13.0	— 9.2		—12.0	—10.0
	3.2	6.7		2.4	3.7
Denmark	18.0	16.6	Switzerland	14.9	17.6
	—10.8	— 9.6		—11.3	— 9.7
	7.2	7.0		3.6	7.9
Finland	19.9	18.4	United Kingdom	15.3	17.5
	—13.0	— 8.9		—12.6	—11.5
	6.9	9.5		2.7	6.0
France	15.0	18.0	U.S.S.R.	no data	24.9
	—15.3	—11.4			— 7.1
	— 0.7	6.6			17.8
Hungary	20.2	14.6	United States	17.1	23.6
	—14.2	—10.2		—11.3	— 9.5
	6.0	4.4		5.8	14.1
Italy	22.9	18.5	Canada	20.0	26.9
	—14.2	— 9.7		—10.3	— 7.8
	8.7	8.8		9.7	19.1
Netherlands	19.8	20.8	Australia	17.4	22.4
	— 8.8	— 7.6		— 9.4	— 8.6
	11.0	13.2		8.0	13.8
Norway	15.1	17.3	New Zealand	17.3	26.4
	—10.4	— 9.1		— 9.1	— 8.8
	4.7	8.2		8.2	17.6
Portugal	26.7	23.9	Japan	30.8	17.2
	—15.8	—10.4		—17.0	— 7.6
	10.9	13.5		13.8	9.6

[a] Statistical Office of the United Nations, *Demographic Yearbook, 1961*, The United Nations, New York, 1961.

TABLE 3. Crude Birth Rates, Crude Death Rates, and Crude Rates of Natural Increase per 1000 for Selection Countries, 1937 and 1960 (Cont.)

	1937	1960			1937	1960
India[b]	33.7	39.1 (*1958*)	Costa	42.2	42.9
	−21.9	−19.2 (*1958*)	Rica	−18.2	− 8.6
	11.8	19.9		24.0	34.3
Israel[c]	41.5	27.1	Mexico	44.1	45.0
	−18.9	− 5.7		−24.4	−11.4
	22.6	21.4		19.7	33.6
Chile	33.5	35.4	Venezuela	33.7	49.6 (est.)
	−24.0	−11.9		−18.1	− 8.0
	9.5	23.5		15.6	41.6

[b] Figures for India in 1937 include only parts of that nation. The 1958 figures are taken from the Indian census. Remember that in the intervening years, India and Pakistan were established as separate and independent nations.
[c] In 1937, these figures applied to Palestine.

A brief perusal of the table reveals that the crude birth rates did not change appreciably in Europe but that the crude rates of natural increase did change as a result of a general and overall decline in the crude death rates. Especially significant is the decline in the death rates for southern and eastern European nations. The relatively high crude birth rates and crude rates of natural increase experienced in the English-speaking former colonial nations is attributable primarily to the boom economies which have characterized these nations since World War II. The Latin American countries reflect yet another trend. Here the birth rates remain exceptionally high but in the 23-year interval, death rates have been reduced dramatically, thus resulting in very high crude rates of natural increase. The causes and effects of these changes are difficult to assess.

Net Reproduction Rates

The meaning of crude birth rates, crude death rates, and crude rates of natural increase in "measuring long-run implications of the current vital position of a group" is obscured by the complexity of trends of growth and decline inherent in age composition and other characteristics of a group. In other words, current birth, death, and increase statistics can be very misleading. They may warrant false optimism as readily as false pessimism. High birth rates may

represent the last manifestation of a dying trend or the first manifestation of a coming trend. In vital statistics, lags between cause
and effect, such as number of births and size of the labor force,
are both common and wide. Age composition, in particular, is the
resultant of numerous components that have their roots in the past.
Age composition, in turn, is one of the most important factors affecting the future vital behavior of a group. Groups may ride high on
the ground swell of passing vigor, or they may hide in temporary
stagnation a future swell the impetus for which is already working
under the surface.

To measure mathematically "the long-run implications of the
current vital position" of a group, statisticians use a device known
as the net reproduction rate. "This rate indicates how fast the population would ultimately grow if the risks of death and the fertility
of each age group remained unchanged and there were no migration.
If the rate is 1.50, it means that current fertility and mortality would
ultimately yield a 50 percent increase per generation of 28 to 30
years; if it is 1.00, they would ultimately yield a stationary population; if it is 0.50," the population would ultimately be cut in half
every generation."[11] Needless to say, the net reproduction rate is the
result of laborious calculations based on the vital behavior of each
age group. It thus clearly reflects the effect of age composition on
future population developments.

Demographic Types

A distinction must be made between two distinct demographic
types, both of which manifest growth. This distinction rests on the
fact that some groups displaying growth are *still* growing, though
tendencies toward decline are at work, whereas others are just beginning to grow, with the real upward spurt only starting. These
two demographic types may be referred to as groups in the stage
of "transitional growth" and of "high growth potential" respectively.
The label for the types faced by prospective decline is marked "in-
cipient decline."

Other types can be distinguished. There are two types of stationary population, one resulting from a balance between high birth
and death rates, the other from a balance between low birth and

[11] Frank W. Notestein and others, *op. cit.*, p. 17.

death rates. Obviously a type marked by actual decline must also
be recognized. As will be brought out in the next section, this type
appears as the result of historical developments in which the mechanical revolution is the chief driving force. Arranged in historical
sequence, these types are shown in Fig. 12.

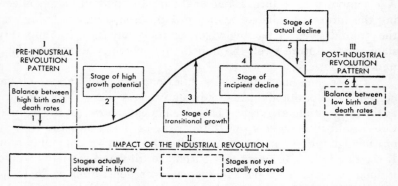

**FIGURE 12. The Impact of the Industrial Revolution on Population
Trends**

Finally, a special demographic pattern or type must be recognized. It may be called the colonial type. It is marked by a high
birth rate, little if at all affected by the sophistications of the West,
and a low—often remarkably low—death rate, definitely the result
of outside interference. Many such nations have birth rates which
may run above the 40 per thousand mark, but have death rates
between 10 and 15, achieved by means of vast expenditures and
patient effort devoted to sanitation, medical care, and improved
ways of living. (Included are many former colonies in Africa and
Latin America.) The crude rate of natural increase—40 minus 10
or 15—is truly phenomenal. Its effect on population increase is
nothing short of explosive. It is bound to aggravate the social problems which the people of these nations face. There is nothing more
worthy of civilized man than to relieve pain, heal the sick, and
prolong life. But if such humane work is to yield the results at which
it is aimed, a wise population policy which considers both births
and deaths, and a courageous economic policy which strives to
create employment opportunities for the surviving millions, are
vitally needed.

THE MECHANICAL REVOLUTION AND POPULATION TRENDS

The World Before 1650

It is generally assumed that the great "vital revolution" or "demographic transition" in the midst of which we are living and the consequences of which are plaguing mankind began around the middle of the seventeenth century. What happened before then is little known, but some basic facts can be conjectured. Growth, on the whole, must have been slow. It must have been slow because high death rates balanced high birth rates. Death rates were high because medicine and sanitation were virtually inoperative, because wars and internecine strife were common experiences, and because human life was worth very little.[12]

The birth rates were correspondingly high. In general, people were living according to the Malthusian rule of "breeding against the means of sustenance," and contraception was little known. What is more, "Any society having to face the heavy mortality characteristic of the premodern era must have high fertility to survive. All such societies are therefore ingeniously arranged to obtain the required births. Their religious doctrines, moral codes, laws, education, community customs, marriage habits, and family organizations are all focused toward maintaining high fertility."[13]

The Great Change

Around 1650, after the Thirty Years' War was finally settled by the Treaty of Westphalia, a number of forces began to act favorably on population growth. The growth came about through a decline of mortality, not an increase of births. "In Europe an era of peace and domestic order began to restore the ravaged continent during the seventeenth century. Then shortly afterward there followed a series of agricultural innovations that greatly increased the food supply, which was further augmented by the vast resources of the New World. Industrial innovations began to bring spectacular

[12] It has been estimated that a young and vigorous slave lasted only two to three years after reaching the mines operated by the Romans in Spain during the Punic Wars. During the transatlantic slave trade whole cargoes of "human ebony" were scuttled to escape capture, and the death rate in transit is supposed to have been horrendous. Infanticide and exposure of the ill and weak were accepted mores in many tribal societies.

[13] Frank W. Notestein, "Population—The Long View," p. 39.

increases in product. Finally, sanitary and medical advances brought control over the ravaging disease of childhood and young adult life. In short, the whole process of modernization in Europe and Europe overseas brought rising levels of living, new controls over disease, and reduced mortality."[14] While beginning with commercial and agricultural development, the movement gained momentum with the coming of the mechanical revolution, the increased use of inanimate energy which in turn fertilized all other fields of economic endeavor.

Thus there began a period of rapid growth, first in northwestern Europe, and spreading from there to central and still later to southern and eastern Europe, Russia, Japan, Latin America, and India. The countries of the world, one after the other, began that strange vital revolution or demographic career mapped out in Fig. 12.

Negative Phase of the Industrial Revolution

The first impact of the mechanical revolution and its forerunners on population was positive. It caused an almost explosive increase in numbers, especially of the white race.[15] This vast growth is shown in Table 4.

But eventually the process of modernization which is here referred to as the mechanical revolution generated powerful negative forces which in due course brought the peoples of the West to the brink of population decline. After a long lag, the process of modernization began to affect fertility and birth rates began to fall. The negative phase of the Industrial Revolution had begun. If high fertility rates were consciously sponsored and guarded by a host of social devices prompted by the specter of high mortality rates, it was only a matter of time until low mortality rates would call for a revision of the ancient codes. Institutions change slowly. Lowering the death rate meets with whole-hearted approval; lowering the birth rate meets with fierce opposition from those who view

[14] *Ibid.*

[15] Condliffe (*op. cit.*, pp. 14–15) comments on this explosive outburst as follows: "It is perhaps salutary to look first at the 19th century increase in the population of western Europe through the eyes of a Chinese. In the first of his famous lectures on 'The Three Principles of the People,' which have become the political bible of modern China, Dr. Sun Yat-sen laid stress on the peril—'the white peril'—which western European and American economic expansion constituted for other peoples, and particularly for China. Very similar statements may be culled from the writings of Indian and Japanese students of population."

TABLE 4. The Increase of Population in Western Europe and European Settlements Overseas, 1800–1960 (in millions)

Country	1800	1850	1900	1960
Belgium	3.0	4.4	6.7	8.5
Denmark	1.0	1.4[a]	2.5	4.4
Finland	1.1	1.6	2.6	4.4
France	28.2	35.8	40.7	42.8
Germany	23.0	35.1[b]	56.4	71.3
West Germany	. . . .	. . . .	. . . .	53.1
East Germany	. . . .	. . . .	. . . .	18.2
Great Britain	10.7	20.9[c]	37.0	52.7
Ireland	5.3	6.6[c] . .	4.5	2.8
Italy	18.1	. . . .	32.5	50.5
Netherlands	2.2	3.1[c]	5.2	9.6
Norway	0.9	1.3[d]	2.2	3.3
Portugal	3.1	3.5[e]	5.4	8.9
Spain	12.0	14.2[fg]	18.6	30.4
Sweden	2.3	3.5	5.1	7.5
Switzerland	1.8	2.4	3.3	5.4
Argentine	. . . .	. . . .	4.0[h]	20.0
Australia	. . . .	1.6[i]	3.7[h]	10.5
Brazil	. . . .	7.7[b]	16.6[h]	70.8
Canada	0.35[b]	2.4[j]	5.4	18.2
Chile	. . . .	. . . .	2.7[h]	7.3
New Zealand	. . . .	. . . .	0.8	2.4
Union of So. Africa	. . . .	. . . .	5.2[k]	15.8
United States	5.3	23.2	76.1	179.3

[a] Not including Schleswig-Holstein. Lauenburg 888,750.
[b] W. F. Willcox, *International Migrations*, p. 77.
[c] 1851.
[d] 1855.
[e] Not including Madeira and Azores, 343,000.
[f] 1849.
[g] Including Balearic and Canary Islands.
[h] Census figures.
[i] E. O. G. Shann, *Economic History of Australia*.
[j] British America, 1901.
[k] 1904.

SOURCES: J. B. Condliffe, *The Economic Pattern of World Population*, Planning Pamphlet No. 18, National Planning Association, Washington, 1943, p. 16; 1800 and 1900 figures from *Encyclopaedia of the Social Sciences*, Vol. 12, p. 244; 1850 figures from Guillaumin, etc., *Annuaire de l'economie politique et de la statistique*, Paris; 1960 figures from *Demographic Yearbook, 1961*, Statistical Office of the United Nations.

parentage as a sacred right, not as one of the highest social responsibilities.

How this reduction of fertility came about is a complicated story still partly veiled in mystery.

There is abundant evidence that the decline came about primarily through rational control, largely by means of contraceptive practices. It does not follow that contraception can be viewed as the cause of the declining birth rate in any profound sense. Relatively effective methods of contraception were widely known for centuries before they were generally used. Birth rates were reduced largely by means of contraception, but in response to drastic changes in the social and economic setting that radically altered the motives and aims of people with respect to family size.[16]

The catalogue of such changes is large and can only be suggested here. Most of them center around the growing individualism and rising levels of popular aspiration developed in urban industrial living. With the growth of huge and mobile city populations, the individual came to depend less and less on the status of his family for his place among his fellows. The station to which he was born gave place to his accomplishments and possessions as the measure of his importance. Meanwhile, the family lost many of its functions to the factory, the school, and commercial enterprises, all these developments made large families a progressively difficult and expensive undertaking; expensive and difficult for a population increasingly freed from older taboos and increasingly willing to solve its problems rather than to accept them. In short, under the impact of urban life, the social aim of perpetuating the family gave way progressively to that of promoting the health, education, and material welfare of the individual child; family limitation became widespread; and the end of the period of growth came in sight. However, during that period the population of European extraction had increased nearly sevenfold throughout the world.[17]

In a way, this negative phase of the Industrial Revolution is as vital as the positive phase. For not only does it spare industrial countries untold woe in the form of vast "technological unemployment," but it accounts for much of the superiority of the modern industrial way of life over the old vegetable coolie pattern. There are those who would deny the possibility of technological unemployment. The reasoning on which they base their argument (ma-

---

[16] See Norman E. Himes, *Medical History of Contraception* (Baltimore: Williams and Wilkins Co., 1936); and Frank W. Notestein and Regina K. Stix, *Controlled Fertility* (Baltimore: Williams and Wilkins Co., 1940, chap. xv).

[17] Frank W. Notestein, *op. cit.*, pp. 40–41.

chines make things cheaper; the cheaper the thing, the larger the demand; the stronger the demand, the more things are made, etc.) is sound enough so far as it goes. But it does not go far enough. Today, a large share of the unemployment in the United States might be termed "technological," a result of automation and other products of the highly advanced technical society.

The great question before mankind today is how fast and how soon this negative phase will spread to other parts of the earth. Our own past furnishes the answer: not until (1) the tremendous pent-up force of high growth potential has been released and spent and (2) the culture level of the masses in the countries now in the "high growth potential" and "transitional growth" stages of the demographic cycle has reached a level high enough to make "a baby grand" seem more desirable than "a grand baby." That, alas, takes time, much time. In the meantime, the pressure from the low-standard areas of rapid growth on the thinly or moderately densely populated areas of the prosperous West will be terrific. The political and military implications of this differential population growth are vast and ominous.

The Modern Demographic Pattern

Before the great discoveries and inventions and the commercial, agricultural, and industrial revolutions stirred vegetating and proliferating humanity from its ancient lethargy, a certain balance was maintained between births and deaths. It was maintained by a high level of both, perhaps an average of 40 births and 35 deaths, or something of that order. Now the world shows signs of a new balance, a new equilibrium. This time it is one marked by low birth rates and lower death rates. So far as the continuity of the group is concerned, it may not make much difference whether the crude rate of increase is the result of subtracting 35 from 40 or 5 from 10. But what a difference this simple arithmetic makes in the fundamental character and performance of civilization! The difference is simply this: an ancient people with a high birth and death rate balance virtually exhausts itself in the biological process of group survival. Much female labor is absorbed in bearing and rearing children. The ratio of productive to unproductive years is pathetic. The labor force constitutes a relatively small portion of the total population. This small force, on whose shoulders rests the responsibility of feeding and otherwise caring for the whole group, is apt to be hard pressed. They turn to children for help. The whole group is overworked. Yet it cannot get ahead. More or less all work is heavy work; there are no typing or telephone jobs for female labor.

Under the high birth and death rate pattern vast numbers of babies are born that never live more than a few weeks or months; others linger for a few years but never reach the age at which they can repay society for the effort and sacrifice which reared them and brought them near but not up to the level of productive strength and ability. While some adults live to a very old age, many die from accidents or diseases after relatively few years of productive labor. The group may be on the brink of bankruptcy because not enough adults can pay their debts to society. The situation is aggravated by the fact that old age comes early after superhuman struggles, and is largely unproductive. Average life expectancy at birth in such a society is very low, perhaps in the twenties or low thirties.

The superiority of modern industrial civilization over ancient vegetable civilization rests largely on the different life expectancy at birth, the age composition which this implies, and the ratio of productive to unproductive members of the group which results from these conditions. A vegetable civilization cannot build up much capital because its inefficient man power exhausts itself in producing food for the wasteful structure of the group. Japan may have lost World War II because her rulers had to keep a vast portion of the population in food production. The situation is worse in China. In the United States the total labor force is much larger relative to the total population, and only a small fraction is employed in agriculture; robots do the heavy work and create infinite employment opportunities at lighter tasks for the weaker members of the group; the strain of bearing and rearing children is far less on society as a whole. All this makes the whole system more productive and yields surpluses and leisure which furnish not only the capital equipment for harnessing natural energies but also the paraphernalia of good government, and funds for training, education, recreation, better health—in short, for all the elements which lift human existence above the drudgery of the coolie and permit that most precious of all occupational specializations, specialization along the lines of man's peculiar aptitudes.

Optimum Population and Population Density

Perhaps the simplest definition of the term optimum population is that it is the ideal man-land ratio. Another is that the optimum population is that population an increase of which produces overpopulation, and a decrease of which produces underpopulation.

But this simplicity is achieved by shifting the burden of definition from optimum population to that of ideal, overpopulation, and underpopulation. Overpopulation may be defined as the man-land ratio at which, *because of excessive numbers of people,* the social economy brings returns in terms of the values the economy strives to achieve. Underpopulation is defined in the same way except that *excessive numbers* is replaced by *insufficient numbers.* The social economy may be considered subject to the law of diminishing returns. Returns may diminish because of an excess or deficiency of any one factor—nature, culture, or man. But the interrelation of the three factors must never be lost sight of.

Because of this, the optimal point of each factor depends on the proportionality of all three factors. Thus, in an industrial civilization that commands many robots the optimum man-land ratio is found at a population density per square mile far below that which a robotless vegetable civilization must maintain. This idea may be expressed in several ways.

1. The population density at which the optimum is attained depends primarily on the amount of foreign energy, particularly inanimate energy, available.

Since foreign energy can be made available only by means of capital equipment, the same principle could be expressed as follows:

2. The population density at which the optimum is attained depends largely on the amount of capital equipment available.

Furthermore, since a low density is compatible with a high civilization only if the sparse population is very mobile, we can express the same idea a third way:

3. The population density at which the optimum is attained depends on the relative mobility of the population.

In view of the close relationship between the supply of inanimate energy, the availability of capital equipment, and the degree of mobility, the first formula may be said to contain the other formulas.

Such principles may appear rather abstract, but they aid the understanding and critical appraisal of national economies and the advantages and limitations of modern mechanical civilization.

One conclusion, however, may be drawn here. Fortunately we do not need to rely on population increase to bring us closer to the optimum. Every improvement in the technique—and, one might add, in the management—of transportation and communication reduces the space handicap, lowers the weight of the overhead burden, and thus brings us closer to the optimum. Too sanguine hopes should not be based on this statement, for one must not lose sight of the fact that population growth is itself a dynamic factor in the process of cultural development. Therefore, what at a given moment may appear as an ideal man-land ratio, viewed as a stage in an unfolding process, may fall short of the ideal. A declining birth rate may lead toward the optimum, but the decline, because of its momentum, may go too far. Population optimum in a machine civilization depends largely on the relationship between mechanical horsepower and human brains, not on acres of pasture land, loaves of bread, and human brawn. This relationship is so complex and dynamic that predictions of future trends seem folly.

BIBLIOGRAPHY

Brown, Harrison, *The Challenge of Man's Future,* New York: The Viking Press, 1954.

Brown, Harrison, James Bonner, and John Weir, *The Next Hundred Years,* New York: The Viking Press, 1957.

Coale, Ansley J. and Edgar M. Hoover, *Population Growth and Economic Development in Low Income Countries: A Case Study of India's Prospects,* Princeton: Princeton University Press, 1958.

Doane, Robert R., *World Balance Sheet,* New York: Harper & Row, Publishers, Inc., 1957.

Gottman, Jean, *Megalopolis,* New York: Twentieth Century Fund, 1961.

Hauser, Philip M. (Ed.), *Population and World Politics.* New York: The Free Press of Glencoe, 1958.

Hauser, Philip M. (Ed.), *The Population Dilemma,* Englewood Cliffs, N.J.: Prentice-Hall, Inc., 1963.

Hauser, Philip M. and Otis Dudley Duncan (Ed.), *The Study of Population,* Chicago: University of Chicago Press, 1959.

Isard, Walter and others, *Methods of Regional Analysis: An Introduction to Regional Science,* New York: John Wiley & Sons, Inc., and the Technology Press of the Massachusetts Institute of Technology, 1960.

Lenica, Jan and Alfred Sauvy, *Population Explosion, Abundance or Famine,* New York: Dell Publishing Company, Inc., 1962.

Osborn, Fairfield (Ed.), *Our Crowded Planet,* New York: Doubleday & Company, Inc., 1962.

Russell, Sir E. John, *World Population and World Food Supplies,* London: George Allen & Unwin, Ltd., 1961.

Sauvy, Alfred, *Fertility and Survival: Population Problems from Malthus to Mao Tse-tung,* New York: Criterion Books, Inc., 1961.

Sax, Karl, *Standing Room Only,* Boston: Beacon Press, 1955.

Spengler, Joseph J. and Otis Dudley Duncan (Eds.), *Population Theory and Policy,* New York: The Free Press of Glencoe, 1956.

Taeuber, Conrad and Irene B., *The Changing Population of the United States,* New York: John Wiley & Sons, Inc. (for Social Science Research Council), 1958.

The Exploding Metropolis (Editors of *Fortune*), New York: Doubleday & Company, Inc., 1958.

9 CULTURE AND RESOURCES

ORIGIN, MEANING, AND FUNCTION OF CULTURE

Man the Culture-Builder

At first there was nature. It included the earth and the sky and the stars in the sky and all that was and lived on the earth—rocks and sand, fauna and flora, earth and water, energy and matter. Then came man; and man alone of all living creatures was given the power to lift himself out of the compass of nature, the right to set his will against the will of nature and to shape nature, or parts of it, to his will to strengthen his hand in his struggle with nature. Thus there arose that lofty edifice which we call culture.

Man alone of all creatures can build culture. Culture building is a human prerogative. It stems from the human capacity to invent arts and artifacts and to elevate arts to the level of science, a capacity that derives from man's superior intellect and unique physical endowment. It is culture that permits man to inhabit every continent, to exist in the tropics and in the frigid zones of the earth. This does not mean that he wipes out the effects of climatic difference on him. His adjustment to climate is only partial. In spite of the latest devices for heating and cooling houses, people still crowd into a few areas of the more temperate zones.

Culture a Joint Product of Man and Nature

Nature and man may be called the original resource factors. Culture is the derivative. It is a joint product of man and nature. Man creates culture with the aid, "advice, and consent" of nature, out of substances found in nature, and with the aid of energies supplied by nature.

That nature aids man in culture building is obvious; it needs no further explanation. But the phrase "the advice and consent" of nature may deserve some comment. As was pointed out in the first chapter, man has a natural bent for economy. He strives to get the

164

most for his effort. Therefore, he does not run head-on against the resistances of nature; as often as not he goes around the obstacle. If nature offers alternatives, man is apt to choose the one that offers the best results for his effort. He chooses to want what nature permits him to produce with the least effort and with the best results for his effort. Europeans eat potatoes, Asiatics eat rice, North Americans eat corn-fed meat. In Europe conditions favor the production of potatoes, in Asia they favor rice, and in North America, corn. This statement is not meant to suggest some simple natural determinism or environmentalism. The point made here is that the desire to economize effort often leads man to adapt himself consciously and willingly to nature. Nature, so to speak, advises man to choose what natural conditions render easiest to produce. Nature does not consent to men living at the North Pole or on the top of Mount Everest.

Culture and Adaptation

Much of culture may be properly viewed as a device of adaptation to nature. But it is more. It permits man to imitate nature. Rayon is a deliberate attempt to imitate the silkworm. Culture permits man to improve on nature. Novocaine is a deliberate improvement on cocaine. Culture enables man to create new substances nowhere found in nature. Nylon and a host of other chemical products fall into this category. Culture gives man the power to release energies not available in nature. The energies of the accelerated fission of fissionable elements, generally called atomic or nuclear energies, are a case in point.

Culture is the sum total of all the devices produced by man, with the aid, "advice, and consent" of nature, to assist him in the attainment of his objectives. The first of these objectives is the survival of the race with the aid of limited supplies and in the face of powerful resistances. As was stressed before, mankind as yet has no collective will. The will to survive is lodged in social groups and may be pushed by one group at the expense of others. The second objective—if one may use the term to apply to an urge, not clearly and consciously planned, but springing from the depth of man's nature—is the provision for expanding populations. Here again there is no global unity, but, on the contrary, national conflict. The third objective is apparently the provision of greater comforts and a better material existence. Finally, culture aims to quench "the thirst that from the soul doth rise," to provide the highest values, the yearning for which is the main distinction between human beings and other living creatures.

Culture and Defects of Nature

From the standpoint of man, nature not only places many obstacles in his path, but appears to possess definite defects as a partner in production. These defects manifest themselves in *insufficient* production, production in the *wrong place*, and production at the *wrong time*. The natural ancestors of our modern cereals were puny grasses bearing little seed. The natural ancestor of our modern cow had a tiny udder, barely sufficient to feed one calf. Spontaneous yields soon proved insufficient as the number of eaters increased. So man cultivated plants and turned them into veritable starch, sugar, and gluten factories; he domesticated animals to raise their output of milk and meat; he cultivated fields to make two blades grow where one grew before; he enhanced the fertility of the soil and provided more water. That is one line of cultural improvement.

Another cultural objective is to move nature's products from the "wrong place" where nature put them to the "right place" where man wants them. The cotton of the South moves to Lancashire and Japan, the mutton of Australia to the cities of England, the oil of the Middle East to the industrial centers of North America and Europe. So the earth is crisscrossed with rail nets, highways, steamship lanes, and skyways. Rivers are bridged, mountains pierced, and isthmuses cut through. A vast amount of effort and substance goes to provide the rolling stock, motor vehicles, ships, and planes that perform the corrective task of bringing things "from where they are to where they ought to be." A third objective of culture is aimed at correcting nature's poor timing. Man wants to eat every day. Nature produces food in rhythmic response to the seasons. So man erects warehouses, elevators, and other storage devices; he develops the art of refrigeration and thus corrects, at least in part, the third defect of nature.

All these corrective efforts require more than mere physical equipment. They call for vast systems of communications, for banking and insurance, and for commercial organizations, wholesale and retail.

Culture and Resistances, Human and Natural

The aspects of nature discussed in the preceding section may be treated under the broader heading of resistances. Culture has the dual function of enlarging resources and reducing resistances. It is a cushioning device that does not abolish hurricanes and earthquakes but cushions the impact of natural disasters on man. "Forewarned is forearmed." Ships advised by radio of an approaching hurricane may be able to avoid it or at least enter the danger zone at the least dangerous angle. But one need not associate natural resistances with catastrophes. Distance is such a resistance. How cultural devices help to overcome that resistance is well known. Friction is another.

As was brought out in the presentation of the functional theory of resources, resistances are by no means confined to nature. There are many human resistances also. (See Table 1.) Culture also functions in the form of education, sanitation, health service, training, church, government, etc. That these phases of culture are lagging behind was discussed in Chapter 3. That culture, moreover, generates its own resistances will be brought out more fully later on.

Culture an Aid to Man and Nature

Culture, a joint product of human effort and ingenuity and of nature, lends aid, in turn, to both man and nature. Just as the arts were divided into those designed to enlarge human capacities and those designed to render nature more amenable to human use (see Chapter 3), so culture, which includes the arts, may be similarly divided into devices designed to support and aid man and nature respectively. The labor-saving machine clearly supports man, and terracing, fertilizers, drainage, bud grafting, and hybridizing help nature to produce more. Both sets of cultural devices may raise the productivity of labor; but the one achieves this goal by aiding man directly, the other by enlarging the product that man, with a given amount of labor, extracts from nature. The man-aiding devices are not all as simple as labor-saving machines. They include intangibles such as management in the widest sense of total coördination of group effort, mores promoting group coöperation, education, training, improved health, and such aids to thinking, planning, and calculating as libraries, laboratory equipment, logarithm tables, "mechanical brains," etc. They even include the division of labor and specialization, arrangements which affect productivity indirectly but nevertheless materially. Recreation, intellectual pursuits, hobbies, spiritual guidance and devotion must not be omitted. For peace of mind, clean thought, and a fresh outlook are vital aids to human performance.

Culture the Equalizing Agent

Culture varies in origin, form, and function according to the character of the natural environment and the relationship between the natural opportunities and the population. In densely populated areas deficient in, or unable to use mineral resources, especially fuels and metals, capital is usually made by man through hard work or abstention; it is applied to the land to raise its yield. Thus in Asia irrigation systems, rice terraces and similar improvements of the land are typical forms of culture. Such tangible forms of culture designed to render more effective the processes of production are generally referred to as capital.

On the other hand, where labor is scarce and natural opportunities for mechanization abound, capital, though invented and designed by man, is made with the aid of inanimate energies. In the United States these conditions were found during the nineteenth century and they in part account for the perfection and accumulation of labor-saving devices. (Time-saving devices also save labor indirectly.) Some sections of Europe resemble Asia, and others America, in this respect.

In short, in the countries relying mainly on man power for energy, where human labor is abundant relative both to the small amount of land that human labor can cultivate without inanimate energy (see Chapter 7) and to the paucity of natural forces that can be tapped, culture in the form of capital tends to be applied to nature in the form of land, farm land—food-yielding, human-energy-creating land. Conversely, in countries where man has succeeded in surrounding himself with many robots—i.e., natural energy units—and where, with the aid of this potent and tireless staff of assistants furnished by nature, he can tap numerous forms and phases of nature with far greater efficiency than can the robotless coolie, nature is abundant and natural forces, guided by man, contribute to erect the structure of culture assisting him.

This equalizing function of culture may be expressed in the form of a "law": The "long" factor (i.e., the abundant factor) tends to create culture (capital) to support the "short" factor.

CULTURE IN THE WORLD TODAY

Culture and the Ecumene

If one understands the ecumene to refer to the areas of the globe inhabited by man, it follows logically that the area of the ecumene is also the area of culture. Wherever man's habitat extends, there culture extends also.

But culture extends beyond the borders of the ecumene. There are desert regions in many parts of the world which once were rich agricultural areas supporting large populations. The jungle of Yucatán covers areas where civilization once flourished. There are ghost towns in the West where cities of considerable size once stood. Though no longer functioning in the service of man, the culture changes wrought by man continue to exert a certain influence. Mountains denuded of their forest cover may be abandoned by man to nature, but the natural landscape continues to show the scars and to reveal the destructive powers of man. The fauna and flora are changed by man's eradication of entire species. The old ecological equilibrium no longer exists.

Moreover, man's cultural reach goes beyond the borders of the ecumene. The oceans are not inhabited by man, but they play an important role in cultural endeavor. The air is not inhabited, but skyways penetrate it in increasing numbers. Man's knowledge and even, in modest ways, his influence reach into interstellar space.

Culture and "The Machine"

Until the coming of the machine the impact of culture on nature, by and large, was superficial. One may say that before the age of industrialization the cultural landscape was a mere modification of the natural landscape. The man who cultivates the field with simple tools leaves the natural landscape still visible through its transparent cultural veneer. The domesticated animal still resembles its wild ancestor; and the roads and highways, generally surfaced with materials found nearby, blend into the landscape. Houses, villages, and towns likewise seem to fit into the picture—a change, to be sure, from original nature but not a violent reversal of natural trends, not a blatant insult flung at nature's face.

The machine, on the other hand, does violence to the landscape. It pushes the culture process to extremes, bringing into existence artifacts which are no longer germane to their natural background. Before the coming of modern machines, technical development reached a limit beyond which man did not seem able to push. For thousands of years he got along with the hand loom, the hammer, the saw; he managed with a few simple machines; he dug his ditches with a spade and used vehicles drawn by animals. As was pointed out before, China today uses techniques born thousands of years ago. Apart from firearms, the printing press, and the compass, European technology of the sixteenth century was but little advanced over that of Greece and Rome. The greatest advance was in the geographical spread of that technology, sweeping eastward as far as Siberia, and westward to America.

This premachine culture, which one may call the ancient culture pattern, resulted mainly from the direct reactions of man to his natural environment. His fields, gardens, forests, cathedrals, monasteries, and cities sprang from his hand and head, unmistakable answers to the inevitable problems created by the natural environment, clear-cut defense mechanisms. This entire ancient culture pattern was functionally true in the sense that it developed in direct response to immediate problems. In the premachine age nature predominated over culture, for man did not dare to subjugate nature.

The coming of the machine changed all this with incredible suddenness. Within a century and a half the process of mechanization has resulted in a new artificial environment, an environment which does not seem to blend into the natural landscape, which does not lie snugly embedded in its natural foundation and organically related thereto, but one which evolves in accordance with laws other than those of organic nature. Mathematical formulas and the laws of physics, chemistry, and mechanics govern today where once the patriarch or the guild master ruled. This new environment is not a part of the cultural landscape; it is an attachment made from foreign stuff.

To appreciate this rather abstract appraisal of the new environment which the machine has created, one will do well to compare a modern factory city with a medieval town. The latter seems to fit well into the landscape. Being built of the surface matter of the earth on which it stands, it blends imperceptibly into its natural surroundings. Not so the modern factory town. In crass contrast with the fields and woods about it, it appears as an intruder from a different world. And so it is; for does it not draw its strength from the bowels of the earth? We may admire the symmetry of modern architecture, and even more its inexorable obedience to human purpose; but nothing can alter its artificiality, nothing can bridge the gap between the wonder of steel and stone, the marvel of human ingenuity which is built according to the laws of dead matter with the aid of inanimate energy, and the world of nature beyond. Surely the modern machine pattern differs as much from the ancient culture pattern as the latter differs from nature itself.

Probably nowhere are purer examples of this modern machine environment found than in the United States—unless it be in the new cities of Soviet Russia where man is trying to accomplish in years what western Europe did in centuries and more than Asia did in millenniums. Perhaps William Allen White did not exaggerate: "The average American is a new thing in the world, a man begotten by machines. Every other kindred or tribe on earth has sprung out of the soil. Other kindreds and tribes have been enriched by some beloved environment, by mountains, by rivers, by high plateaus, or desert wastes, and to these topographical manifestations the hearts of other people lay claim. But for 300 years, the American has been on the move, trying to find his ultra-western horizon."[1] Being on the move, he could not take root. Thus the machine, the symbol of devitalized artificiality, and not the soil, the transmuting agent of organic nature, is shaping the physiognomy of this, the newest civilization.[2]

Culture and Agriculture

While the impact of the machine on the natural landscape stands out by its almost brutal violence, the cultural changes wrought

[1] *The New York Times* Magazine Section, January 4, 1931, p. 18.
[2] This discussion of the machine environment is in part based on E. Diesel, *Das Land der Deutschen*, Bibliographisches Institut. A. G., Leipzig, 1932.

in the world of living plants and animals can be easily underrated. These changes in fauna and flora date back to the earliest recorded history. Even in ancient times man transferred crops from one region to another, even from one continent to another. The greater mobility of modern man has vastly aided and accelerated the work of the plant and animal explorers. Moreover, their work is aided by plant and animal breeders as never before. The science of genetics, although relatively young, is performing miracles in adapting fauna and flora to man's needs.

South America furnishes striking illustrations of the extent to which natural fauna and flora have been changed by man. The Andes are considered the original habitat of the white potato and the cinchona tree from whose bark quinine is obtained. Today the north European plain is the center of potato culture and Indonesia has a virtual monopoly of quinine production. South America was the original habitat of cacao and hevea rubber. Today the bulk of the former is grown in Africa; of the latter, in the Malay peninsula, Indonesia, and neighboring areas. Conversely, almost all the major crops found in South America today, as well as the most important animals, were brought in from the outside. Sugar cane, coffee, wheat, rice, sheep, hogs cattle are all of foreign origin. They have remade the landscape, at least its most productive phases.

Similarly, the South of the United States illustrates the importance of alien plants and animals. Neither horses nor sheep nor cattle nor pigs were known in North America before the landing of Columbus. The crossbreeding of cattle brought in from Europe with zebu (Brahman) cattle from India is another example of cultural modification of fauna. Cotton, the tyrant that long ruled the South, was an outlander, though possibly there was a Caribbean branch of the family tree. Tobacco, one of the few native crops, never became king. Corn, or maize, which had been brought in from Central America, until recently lingered in modest circumstances in the South while flourishing farther north, farther away from its original habitat. Now that heroic efforts are being made to rewin the South after it came close to ruin under the reign of King Cotton, what are the crops on which the soil rebuilder relies most? Soybeans from Manchuria, kudzu from Japan, alfalfa and lupin from Asia, and purple clover from Europe.

Undoubtedly one of the most significant impacts of culture on the natural landscape is to be seen in the work of the railroad in converting almost uninhabitable plains and prairies into the granaries of the modern world. These granaries are the western counterpart of the rice terraces of Asia. One is the work of steam, the other the work of sweat, sweat of millions of men and women and children toiling in the steaming valleys of monsoon Asia. The replacement of short and long grasses of the plains and prairies by cereals, alfalfa, and other nitrogen-fixing forage crops is probably the most magnificent change wrought by culture-building man in the natural landscape. The countries most affected by the plains-opening miracle were the United States, Canada, Argentina, the Soviet Union and her satellites, Hungary and Rumania, and to a much lesser extent, Australia. That such wondrous change was not achieved without grave errors of judgment followed by grave disaster at the hands of revengeful nature is well known. But man does seem to be able to learn from his mistakes, cynical interpreters of history notwithstanding.

Culture and Human Attitudes

So far, the effects of culture on nature have been discussed. Some of the most vital effects of culture are those on man himself. Culture means education, learning, experience, religion, civilized behavior, suppression of vicious animal instincts, coöperation replacing conflict, the law of fair play and justice suppressing the law of the jungle.

Culture even affects the most intimate of human mores, those governing reproduction. When culture reaches higher levels, unrestrained breeding against the means of sustenance yields to birth control and planned parenthood.

THE ANATOMY OF CULTURE

Material and Nonmaterial (Spiritual) Culture

Culture is such a vast and complex concept that it defies orderly classification. However, some attempts along this line will be made. In the first place, the distinction between material and nonmaterial culture, indirectly touched upon in the preceding discussion, deserves closer attention.

Nonmaterial culture is more changeable. Though mind and

matter are too different to admit of comparison, in a deeper sense it may be said that the modern mind differs from that of antiquity more completely than the cultural landscape of today differs from its ancient counterpart. The importance of such events as the coming of Christ, the Crusades, the great discoveries, and the Renaissance lies more in the realm of the mind than in the fields of art and architecture in which are manifested the tangible results. The difference between a modern Calvinist and a worshiper of Buddha or between a modern manufacturer and a Roman industrialist is more vital than the difference between an automobile and a Roman chariot. Historical sense, the injection of scientific thought into ever-wider investigation and endeavor, the capitalistic spirit with its worship of profits, and particularly the ethical concepts of social responsibility are as vital innovations as railroads, steamships, or automobiles. The two changes—tangible and intangible—go hand in hand and together remake the world of nature into a world which represents an inextricable interpenetration of nature and culture.

Rarity of "Natural" Resources

At this advanced stage of human history so much culture has been added and worked into nature that it is well-nigh impossible to segregate the "natural" resource from the cultural. For example, take virgin soil fertility. Is there anything more "natural" than that? But its function as a resource depends very largely upon the particular use which man makes of it at a given place and time. Can we say that the soil fertility which is lodged in a certain area connected with a market by means of modern transportation is wholly natural? As was pointed out before, to function as a resource the soil fertility must be correlated with the man-made transportation agency. Take the case of the forests. It might be possible to find a primeval forest which is a natural resource in the pure and undiluted sense of the word, but it would be difficult. In most of the older countries, whatever forests are left are either better or worse because of human interference with natural growing conditions. Thus, a good portion of what in popular parlance goes under the name of natural resources, reveals cultural aspects upon more critical scrutiny. Moreover, if resources are merely expressions of the human appraisal of nature, how can the human element be eliminated from the resource concept? For the human appraisal depends as much upon man's objectives and upon his mental and physical abilities, his general capacity to make use of his environment, as upon the nature of the environment. Any change, therefore, which goes on in the human mind, which affects the organization of society, which influences the aims of resource utilization, injects into the resource aspects of nature a human element which is inseparable from it.

Natural and Cultural Environments

The environment must therefore be viewed as consisting of at least two distinct elements: the natural and the cultural. Since culture is a social product, that is, an achievement of group coöperation, we may refer to cultural environments as social environments or the social heritage. Man shares the natural environment with all animals, but man alone possesses the capacity to create cultural or social environments. Through culture he has softened the rigors of nature. By superimposing the structure of social environments on nature, he has continuously expanded the habitable area of the globe until today even the Arctic and Antarctic regions must accustom themselves to his sight.

Through this intermingling of natural and cultural aspects the environment of modern man has grown so much in complexity that classification has become exceedingly difficult. The following, however, is one that repays careful study. It was worked out by the well-known sociologist, L. L. Bernard.[3]

I. THE NATURAL ENVIRONMENTS, or the untransformed aspects of nature:

a. *The inorganic environment*—consisting of cosmic materials and processes, physical geography, soil, climate, the inorganic resources, natural agencies and natural mechanical processes.

b. *The organic environment*—consisting of micro-organisms, various parasites and insect pests, plants, animals, ecological and symbiotic relationships of plants and animals, the prenatal environment of man, and natural biological processes.

II. THE SOCIAL ENVIRONMENTS OF THE FIRST ORDER, or those physical transformations of nature which enable the organism to adjust itself

[3] L. L. Bernard, "Mind—Its Emergence as a Mechanism of Adjustment," chap. 26 of F. A. Cleveland and collaborators, *Modern Scientific Knowledge*, The Ronald Press Company, New York, 1929. Also "A Classification of Environments," *American Journal of Sociology*, November, 1925.

more effectively and economically, although more indirectly, to the natural environments:

a. *The physico-social environment*—consisting of physical inventions, illustrated by tools, machines, houses, shelter, means of transportation and communication, cities, artificial ice, fire, clothing, instruments for scientific research, etc.

b. *The bio-social environment*—consisting of the natural organic environment as modified by training and by plant and animal breeding. Examples of this form of the social environment are domesticated plants and animals, pets, slaves, trained servants, and laborers, artisans, athletes, students, soldiers, etc.

III. The Social Environments of the Second Order, or the psycho-social environments, based upon language symbols and communication:

a. *The psycho-social environment,* dependent upon *gesture language*. The content of this phase of the psycho-social environment is relatively meager. It begins in the lowest stages of savagery, but persists into the present.

b. *The psycho-social environment,* dependent upon *vocal language*. The experiences of men are symbolized verbally and communicated from one person to another until they become common possessions. These common or collective experiences are made objective through language and they take on the forms of traditions, customs, folkways, conventions, beliefs, mores, proverbs, maxims, public opinion, etc.

c. The third aspect of the *psycho-social environment* to develop appeared with the introduction of *written language*. The vocal forms of the psycho-social environment continue to function broadly along with the written forms and probably outnumber the latter. The written content is carried through books, newspapers, phonograph records, movie films, and pictures. It takes the form chiefly of poetry, drama, fiction, art, essays, history, laws, codes, philosophy, and the sciences. The sciences especially could not exist except for this written or printed medium, and they are the basis of our modern civilization. Without the sciences, both theoretical and applied, we could not have our industry, medicine, sanitation, hygiene, political institutions, and the other highly developed forms of social organization and control.

IV. The Derivative-Control and Institutional Environments. These are composite environments, made up of all forms and varying degrees of organization. But they are dominated particularly by the psycho-social environments.

Here the cultural modifications of nature are viewed as expressions of human adaptation to the environment. These adaptations are simple and direct in the early stages of social evolution, but become increasingly complex and indirect as societies grow larger and more articulate. As we study Bernard's classification, we see rising before our eyes a lofty edifice, stories piled upon stories, resting on a physical basis not of matter alone but also of energies, of processes, of relationships. Firmly linked to this natural foundation are the first stories, direct adaptation to and modification of physical nature. As the structure rises in height, the contact with physical nature becomes less direct and the purely man-made artificial cultural aspects gain in importance.

Direct and Indirect Adjustments

On the basis of their relative closeness to nature, cultural environments may be divided into direct adjustments to nature and derivative or indirect adjustments. Much culture can be readily explained as the result of the direct adaptation to situations found in the natural environment. More or less all primitive culture is of this nature. A kindled fire involves a cultural change in the natural environment. If this fire serves to keep man warm it is properly called a direct adjustment to the environmental condition of cold. Any artificial shelter belongs in this category. If man's naked hand is too weak to crush a stone and if the same hand can perform this task when armed with a hammer or an ax, the invention and production of such tool-weapons is a direct adjustment to the natural environment.

If, however, in order to get the best results from a machine tool which makes parts used in manufacturing motor trucks, alloy steel must be invented and produced to assure a sharp cutting edge at high temperatures, the adaptation to the natural environment is still there, but it has lost its directness and can only be traced step by step through the various stages of a highly complex process. The high-speed tool-steel may then be called an indirect or a derived adjustment.

Societal institutions are also adaptations to the environment, but they are generally so indirect and sophisticated that the connection is not easily realized. Man discovered early that he could defend himself against wild beasts better in groups than in individual combat, and he therefore developed institutions for social coöperation in a more or less direct adaptation to the natural environment. However, as the groups grow in size and complexity, many institutions develop which, though still remotely related to the original idea of group coöperation, are essentially derivatives of previous institutional adjustments. Man, rationalizing and philosophizing about his original adjustment, often creates derived institutions which show little trace of a direct adjustment to environmental situations. It may not be too difficult to trace the ideas of Jeffersonian democracy to conditions which were determined by the natural environment as they existed in the time of Thomas Jefferson. It is well to remember, however, that Jefferson's mind, far from being a *tabula rasa,* was in reality a rich depository of previous cultural adjustments and showed innumerable imprints of adjustments which the English people, as well as others, had made in the past. But it is very difficult to trace to their natural environment the ideas of a "Democratic" politician of today who uses or abuses Jeffersonian principles merely as accepted formulas of political behavior. This example must suffice to illustrate the lack of a direct and evident connection between many institutions and environments.

Bernard's terminology provokes further comment. As was stated before, he views culture as a structure rising in tiers upon a basis of nature. It is interesting to note that in his division of the natural environment into organic and inorganic, he recognizes what was here called the basic dualism of nature.

Bernard divides cultural environments into three main tiers:
1. Social environments of the first order.
2. Social environments of the second order.
3. Derivative-control and institutional environments.

The last may be viewed as a social environment of the third order. The social environment of the first order is divided into the physico-social and the bio-social environment, thus clearly reflecting the basic dualism just mentioned. Physico-social adjustments are those made to the inorganic (here meaning the non-living) agents of nature, whereas the bio-social adjustments are those made to aspects of living nature. Bernard logically includes men in this category. He thus cuts right across the basic dualism and carries this fundamental dichotomy of the natural environment over to the first-order social environment which, being an environment of direct adjustment to nature, necessarily shares the dualism with nature. This dichotomy is lost in the higher tiers of cultural environment.

Bernard refers to these environments as psycho-social environments. Naturally all cultural environments are social environments because culture is a social product, the social heritage. They are called *psycho*-social—as distinguished from physico-social and bio-social on the lower level—to stress the fact that on this upper level nature no longer acts directly in a straight-line fashion, on an *ad hoc* basis so to speak; now the human mind—the psyche—enters the reaction as an independent and modifying factor. Man reacts no longer with a clean slate; the slate has been written on. The mind is grooved with impressions. These impressions were made in talking over problems with others, overhearing others, and remembering.

Thus communication becomes a vital factor in the development of the psycho-social environment. As communication advances from the halting and unsatisfactory level of gestures and sign language to the higher level of written language, when books and libraries come into vogue, cultural adaptation comes progressively more under the influence of established crystallized human thought and seeks adjustments not to nature directly, but to a growing accumulation of previous human reactions to experiences in life. A man with a classical education will see current issues through different eyes than does a person trained in the natural sciences.

This increased indirectness, this widening of the gap between first impression and final reaction, logically leads, on the top level of derivative control and institutions, to the miraculous achievements of an Einstein on the one hand, and to the confusion of the human mind so characteristic of the modern age. Yet this confusion is not a new invention. Did not the ancient Greeks complain: "What harasses men is not so much the facts themselves as human thoughts (dogmas) on facts"?

THE DIVERSITY OF CULTURES

Human Culture and Cultures

Up to this point human culture has been treated as a sort of collective abstraction, a composite reaction of mankind to its environment. In reality, of course, there is no such abstraction as man. There are only men, women, and children. These men, women, and children live in social groups that develop their own cultures in separate culture areas. These cultures, having evolved out of reactions and adaptations to diverse environments, differ as these environments differ.

During the early stages of human existence, such cultural developments occurred in airtight compartments. As contacts increased and various group interrelations ensued—submission, conquest, merging through intermarriage, etc.—cultures lost some of this pristine simplicity, and blended or alloyed cultures developed. On a still higher level, the cultures of earlier civilizations became the object of deliberate study, as have Egyptian, Greek, Roman, and other ancient cultures, especially since the Renaissance. Likewise, a deliberate effort has been made to explore the contemporary cultures of other ethnic groups. Thus culture takes on a more complex character, and adaptation to local phenomena and solution of local problems yield some of their earlier influence to outside forces.

Problems of Cultural Impingement

These intergroup contacts tend to enrich cultures and help to accelerate their growth. But they also create serious problems. One of the best examples of this danger is Japan. For centuries the Japanese deliberately kept foreign influence to a carefully regulated minimum. Then under the guns of Commodore Perry they were forced to give up their policy of isolation and, realizing the material superiority of the West, especially in warfare, they decided to submit to a deliberate process of westernization. But values which one group of people have built up in a slow and painful process of accretion through the centuries cannot be acquired at will as one buys a gadget in a store. They can be acquired only by retracing slowly and patiently the steps that led the culture-lenders up the steep slopes of Parnassus. How the attempt to borrow certain aspects of western culture while staunchly refusing to accept others led to a sinister hybrid culture and to a tragic end is one of the great lessons of history.

Cultures possess a certain inner coherence and inner logic. They cannot be chopped to pieces without killing the soul. Hence their transfer from one part of the globe to another, from one social group to another, is not to be undertaken in a spirit of levity, but calls for deep understanding of cultural values.

An Example of Culture Transfer

How delicate is the problem of culture transfer may be illustrated by the relationship between the United States and Puerto Rico. The following quotation is taken from a report prepared by the author in the capacity of Director of Research of the Interdepartmental Committee on Puerto Rico appointed by President Franklin Delano Roosevelt early in 1939. During the time that has elapsed since it was written many important changes have occurred; for instance, we can no longer speak of Puerto Rico's labor market as "hermetically-sealed," nor can we say there is "neither immigration nor emigration to speak of." But it remains a good example of the problem of culture transfer between heterogeneous environments.

> While it is true . . . that the problem of Puerto Rico is one of old standing and that, therefore, the entire responsibility for the present troubles cannot be charged to recent policies and administrative measures, the partial responsibility for Puerto Rican difficulties of the Government of the United States is inescapable.
>
> That commercial opportunities largely determine the profit at which products can be sold, and that profit, in turn, affects the flow of capital investment, has been pointed out. The vital importance under these conditions of commercial opportunities in the shaping of productive power is self-evident. In the case of Puerto Rico, the extent of commercial opportunities is largely determined by United States policy. Over that policy the people of Puerto Rico have little control. To a large extent, therefore, the commercial destiny, and through it, the economic and social destiny of the Island is in the hands of the policymakers in Washington. So convinced were the lawmakers of the early nineteenth century of the all-saving grace of industrialization under tariff protection, that they viewed incorporation of Puerto Rico in the tariff system of the United States, in other words, the policy of "assimilation," as an all-embracing and dependable guarantee of Puerto Rican economic progress.
>
> Looking back, it now appears that a policy based on this simple formula may not have been the wisest approach to the problem of Puerto Rico. In these stirring years when the United States extended its sovereign power to outlying possessions, there was neither time nor inclination to probe into the differences between the needs of a tropical island and those of a giant economy of continental expanse. In retrospect, with the lessons of forty years to draw upon, these differences can now be clearly discerned. In the briefest form, they

may be shown in the following outline which suggests some of the most salient points of difference:

Island	*Mainland* (especially during the formative period of economic development)
1. Small size; island.	1. Large size; continent.
2. Conflict between agrarian and aristocratic survivals of Spanish origin with modern commercial and financial industrialization, largely of Anglo-Saxon origin.	2. Relative absence of such conflicts.
3. Little room for expansion.	3. Expanding elbow room.
4. High population density.	4. Generally moderate population density.
5. Paucity of resources, limiting diversity of economic activities.	5. Wealth of resources, permitting great diversity of economic activities.
6. Lack of mineral resources and resultant limitation of mechanization and mobilization.	6. Mineral resources permitting mechanization and mobilization.
7. Low living standards conducive to unrestricted propagation.	7. High living standards conducive to restricted propagation.
8. Relative isolation.	8. Numerous contacts between all parts of the Mainland.

Space does not permit the full development of each of these points of contrast. The last point, however, is so frequently overlooked that at least a few words of comment are called for.

In respect to the degree of isolation or adequacy of contacts, Puerto Rico is not comparable to non-insular (i.e., continental), domestic sugar-producing areas. Such a comparison is sometimes made to appraise the relative dependence on sugar of Puerto Rico and continental domestic sugar-producing areas respectively. Such a comparison is not valid, for the reason that continental domestic sugar-producing areas constitute mere fragments of States whose resources are infinitely more varied than those of Puerto Rico.

The Island is practically a hermetically-sealed labor market; there is neither immigration nor emigration to speak of. While thus the external mobility of Puerto Rican labor is practically zero, the mobility of the labor in continental sugar-producing areas is not inconsiderable. The same difference exists with regard to cultural contacts. In this respect, also, Puerto Rico, for reasons of distance, language, lack of educational facilities, etc., is far more isolated than continental sugar-producing areas. Puerto Rico is a sugar-producing area and little more. It cannot be compared with entire States of the Union. Neither is the comparison between Puerto Rico and other domestic sugar-producing areas valid.

The major implication of this juxtaposition of contrasting features is this: measures and policies adapted to the continental economy with its diversity of resources and multiplicity of alternate occupations, by their very nature, may prove, and in many instances have proved, ill-adapted to the Island's economy, endowed with limited resources and lacking room for expansion. This means that measures and policies devised for and adapted to the Mainland should, as a rule, not be extended to an essentially different economy without proper allowance for these essential differences. Blanket policies and laws covering both the continental economy of the Mainland and the insular economy of Puerto Rico are definitely dangerous unless, at all times, basic differences of needs and opportunities of the two economies are clearly kept in mind.

As was stated before, the basic policy adopted by the United States upon acquisition of Puerto Rico was the policy of "assimilation"; that is, the policy of assimilating the Island to the Mainland by treating it virtually as part and parcel of the continental economy. The most outstanding features of that policy are "free trade" between the Island and the Mainland, and the extension of the United States tariff to Puerto Rico. That policy should now be carefully scrutinized with due regard to essential differences of needs and opportunities in general, and to differences of density and rate of growth of population, and cultural backgrounds in particular.

The difference in population density is important. Its significance appears clear-cut against the background of historical perspective. Throughout its economic development up to the post-war period, there existed in the continental United States a chronic labor shortage. Attracted to this labor vacuum, millions of Europeans migrated to America. At the same time, labor-saving devices were developed to relieve the labor shortage still further. Such labor-saving devices grew spontaneously out of the cultural environment of the North American continent; they could not have developed spontaneously in an over-crowded tropical island. To Puerto Rico, labor-saving devices are essentially foreign. The grafting of exogenous arts and institutions on Puerto Rico must proceed with caution.[4]

[4] Erich W. Zimmermann, *Staff Report to the Interdepartmental Committee on Puerto Rico* (multigraphed), Washington, 1940.

CRITIQUE OF CULTURE

Good and Bad Culture

The tacit assumption is that Homo sapiens does not willingly spoil his own environment and that, on the contrary, cultural changes represent improvements in the natural landscape, improvements in this sense reflecting a better adaptation of nature to human needs. As civilization becomes more complex, however, the dangers of misdirected effort and poor judgment, and at times an even complete lack of comprehension of the best interests of man, increase. Such errors of judgment may appear in the form of idle factory equipment which was never really needed, or of a barge canal never justified by social requirements, or of desolate ridges once heavily wooded but now disfigured by the scars of erosion. The error or lack of judgment may be due to an inadequate understanding of ecology, to an insufficient regard for the future, or to the inability to master the growing complexities of world economy. But above all it is due to man's refusal to reconcile properly the conflicting interests between opposing groups and between the present and the future. Hence, what may appear as culture from the standpoint of short-run private property interests may not be culture in the light of long-run social welfare.

Conflicting Cultures and Relativism

As technology achieves supersonic speed in flight and under the impact of modern science space shrinks and the globe appears smaller and smaller, people find themselves crowded even closer together. There was a time when the intelligentsia of the West committed the fatal error of thinking that this bringing people closer together physically would automatically bring them closer together spiritually as well. The brotherhood of man was considered a simple by-product of fast transport. But crowding people increases the areas of and opportunities for friction, and friction generates heat. Human beings are cantankerous creatures, and the stranger has always been viewed with suspicion. The least departure from local norms is a cause of ridicule and easily leads to blows. Good neighborliness is a difficult art, hard to learn. It can be learned only with endless patience and an amount of tolerance that is not easily acquired. Humanity collectively faces a tremendous task of self-education.

Moreover, there is a real problem to be solved in connection with intercultural tolerance. How can a world society emerge from the welter of fanatic nationalism? Herskovits[5] advocated a creed of cultural relativism when he said: "If a world society is to emerge from a conflict of nationalism, it can only be on a basis of live and let live, a willingness to recognize the values that are to be found in the most diverse ways of life." To this anthropologist, cultural relativism was a "philosophy which, in recognizing the values set up by every society to guide its own life, lays stress on the dignity inherent in every body of custom, and on the need for tolerance."

Culture and Morals

This leads to the role of morals in the shaping of cultural values. In the view of many leaders, the present world crisis is caused by a loss of moral values. The belief that morals derived their force from assumed metaphysical or supernatural foundations is disappearing; morals seem to have no foundation at all. Hence, the loss of moral faith and the crisis in the human spirit. This crisis may be resolved when man realizes the basic truth—that the laws of human nature are as objective as the laws of all nature.

BIBLIOGRAPHY

Bagby, Philip, *Culture and History; Prolegomena to the Comparative Study of Civilizations*, Berkeley: University of California Press, 1959.

Burke, Redmond A., *Culture and Communication Through the Ages*, Chicago: De Paul University, 1953.

Chase, Stuart, *Live and Let Live*, New York: Harper & Row, Publishers, Inc., 1960.

de Grazia, Sebastian, *Of Time, Work, and Leisure*, New York: The Twentieth Century Fund, 1962.

Erasmus, Charles J., *Man Takes Control*, Minneapolis: University of Minnesota Press, 1961.

[5] Melville J. Herskovits, *Man and His Works, The Science of Cultural Anthropology*, Alfred A. Knopf, New York, 1948.

Herskovits, Melville J., *Acculturation: The Study of Culture Contact,* Gloucester, Mass.: P. Smith Company, 1958.

Herskovits, Melville J., *The Human Factor in Changing Africa,* New York: Alfred A. Knopf, 1962.

Kluckhohn, Clyde (Ed.), *Culture and Behavior,* New York: The Free Press of Glencoe, 1962.

Meier, Richard L., *A Communications Theory of Urban Growth,* Cambridge: The M.I.T. Press (for The Joint Center for Urban Studies of the Massachusetts Institute of Technology and Harvard University), 1962.

Oliver, Robert T., *Culture and Communication,* Springfield, Illinois: Thomas, 1962.

10 OBSERVATIONS ON RESOURCE PATTERNS

This chapter brings little new, little that in one way or another has not been touched upon in the preceding chapters. The interaction of nature, man, and culture has been stressed again and again, as has the bearing of energy uses on resource development in general and on factoral proportionality in particular. The contrasts between oriental vegetable and occidental machine civilizations were mentioned repeatedly. In this chapter the rather loose ends of these various interresource relationships are gathered for a brief but systematic analysis.

THE MECHANICAL REVOLUTION AND WORLD RESOURCE PATTERNS

The mechanical revolution furnishes the key to the modern global layout of resource patterns. In the world of today peoples differ in nothing more than in the use of inanimate energy, of the capital equipment which harnesses it, and of the science which renders it efficient. They differ in many other respects, and in vital respects at that, but the use of inanimate energy and all it implies in terms of cultural change and impact on the availability of natural agents supplies the key to understanding these differences.

The power-driven machine raises the productivity both of labor and of nature. This increased productivity in turn permits the accumulation of surpluses over and above consumers' immediate needs. Capital equipment becomes an increasingly vital part of the production process. This equipment is made largely of metals and other inorganic matter taken from the subsoil strata of the earth. Mining for metals and for nonmetallic minerals including the fossil fuels becomes a major occupation of man, as do building machines and factories to house the machines and generating power to drive them. The power-driven machine thrives on large-scale full-time utilization—the major desideratum of "overhead economy"—and hence needs wide markets in which to sell its mass output; it draws on the four corners of the earth for the materials which go into its products. Thus transportation and communication, and the building and maintaining and operating of vast rail nets, steamship lines, and air transport facilities, become vital parts of the economy. Marketing the vast output of factories and power-supported farms gives employment to millions in storing, moving, trading, insuring, financing the vast output of mine, field, and factory. Robots replace men more and more in the actual processes of production. Vice versa, the complex social economy[1] calls for ever-increasing numbers of people engaged in service activities, including the professions and government. The gainful occupations in the modern world include primary, secondary, and tertiary activities. Primary economic activities include agriculture, forestry, and fishing; secondary economic activities cover mining, manufacturing, construction, and the generation of power—in short, the tangible aspects of industry; tertiary (or service or contributory) activities embrace services of both a business and nonbusiness nature, including transport, trade, finance, advertising, personal services, professions, government, etc. Countries differ tremendously in respect to the relative importance of these three major categories. There is a striking negative correlation between income level and prominence of primary activity.

If it is remembered that machine-powered science-aided agriculture in the industrialized countries, far from being "primary" in the original sense, is in reality secondary and tertiary activity functioning indirectly in and through agriculture, it will be realized that actually the contrasts are even sharper than the occupational statistics reveal. The fact that half the working population of leading industrial countries is occupied in tertiary service activities will come as a surprise to many. It is a clear indication of the extent of interdependence and indirectness in the modern social economy.

Recent Changes in the Industrial Map

The mechanical revolution began in England, spread to the continent of Europe, flourished there in a sharply delineated area

[1] By social economy is meant an interdependent economic system marked by interregional and occupational specialization. The opposite is the "anarchic" economy, a loose agglomeration of largely independent local units like the Chinese *hsien* mentioned in chap. 7.

of the northwestern and central regions, and then jumped the Atlantic to the northeastern section of the United States.

These oldest centers of industrialization remain by far the most important ones. But there are other centers of increasing importance. There is Japan, highly industrialized and successful in spite of the effects of World War II. There are sections of India, Australia, eastern and southern Europe, and some parts of Latin America and Africa, which have experienced at least the beginning of industrialization.

One of the most important industrialized countries is the Soviet Union. Emerging with new revolutionary zeal after a series of painful defeats, that country by feverish effort managed to telescope industrial development so that today it ranks second only to the United States as an industrial power.

But there are degrees of industrialization, and industries differ in general character and especially in the extent to which they substitute inanimate energy for human. Much of Latin American, Asiatic, and African industrialization is of a low-order type represented by such manufacturing as textile and food processing which is elevated only little above agricultural activity and depends on large numbers of labor modestly supported by robots.

The Economic Exclave

A peculiar phenomenon associated with the spread of the mechanical revolution is the economic exclave.[2] An economic exclave may be defined as a splinter of one economy lying inside another economy. The economy of the United States is an entity, a social-political-economic entity. Some oil fields of Venezuela, some copper mines of Chile, although lying inside foreign economies, may be viewed as splinters or exclaves of the economy of the United States. The emergence of the exclave is a logical corollary of the differential economic development of different countries. Venezuela had neither the know-how nor the capital to develop its oil deposits and process the oil, nor the market in which to sell the refined products. This was true also of Chile with regard to nitrate. So long as Chilean interests had a world monopoly in the sale of that mineral, ineffi-

---

[2] The term exclave is borrowed from political science where it refers to a splinter of territory which politically belongs to one sovereign state but geographically lies inside the borders of another.

cient methods of production could be followed and Chileans could engage in nitrate production and sale. When that monopoly ended, only efficient, scientific, highly capitalized methods could survive the new competition with sulfate of ammonia and synthetic nitrogen. The nitrate mines were either shut down or converted into exclaves of the United States and British economies.

Economic exclaves are scattered over the earth, although this is less true today than it was 25 years ago. Often they are a thorn in the side of the natives, whose nationalistic pride is injured and who do not cherish the idea of having foreigners exploit the stuff that nature happened to deposit in their backyard. Vigorous efforts have been made to nationalize these exclaves, some with success, as the areas recently assured of political freedom seek their economic freedom as well. This is not as easy as some assume, however.

When thinking of exclaves, one is apt to turn first to minerals. However, the golden belt of plantations which runs along the equator is full of exclaves producing bananas, vegetable oils, fibers, dyewoods, tanning materials, and the like.

RESOURCE PATTERNS AND WORLD WAR II

Extent and Rapidity of Change

We live in an era of rapid and penetrating change. Technology and science never rest. Their restlessness is communicated to processes and industries and reflected in an ever-changing map of world resources.

Superimposed upon the deep and rapid changes wrought by technology and science are the changes wrought by war. For instance, Great Britain, the world power of the nineteenth century, has slipped in power and prestige. With its economic destiny based upon world trade and world finance, Britain has suffered as a result of two world wars and peacetime chaos. In a sense, old historical relationships were reversed. Western and central Europe lost, whereas North America and the Soviet Union, to some extent, gained. The investment streams of the nineteenth century have moved in the opposite direction, especially as evidenced in the Marshall Plan and continued United States spending in Europe. Burke's eloquent phrase, the children offering their full breasts to the aging mother, is implemented by reality.

Delaisi's World Picture

In 1929, the Frenchman Delaisi painted a vivid picture of the earth as it looked to him. He imagined Europe divided into two sharply differing segments[3] which he called Europe A and Europe B (see Fig. 13) and which he described as follows:

> Europe A is covered with a network of railways and highways; travel and trade flourish; it is the land of factories and horsepower. Clothes and lives of men are uniform. With the exception of narrow frontier strips where Polish, Czech or Italian is spoken, only three languages are used: English, French, and German, and that in spite of the fact that eleven states are covered. Europe A is an immense animal organism with functions both specialized and centralized, with cells interdependent, from family to factory or bank.
>
> Europe B stands in sharp contrast: highways and railways are few and far between; old customs survive as well as costumes and dialects. It is like a polyp made up of millions of tiny animals living an independent life on the coral reef which they have built up through the centuries. Europe A, a great vertebrate; Europe B, a polyp.[4]

Whence the difference? The mechanical revolution or, as Delaisi calls it, the "horsepower" revolution (the irony of the phrase is appalling!) has industrialized Europe A, in part even its agriculture, while Europe B has retained its exclusive rural character. Horsepower enables man to produce more and to consume more. According to Delaisi, "The potential wealth of nations does not depend upon the number of inhabitants, but upon the number of horse-powers at their disposal." The United States and Russia have populations of somewhat comparable size, but the United States has many times more horsepower per capita and is infinitely more wealthy. Similarly, a comparison could be drawn between Belgium, with 9 million people and powerfully equipped with horsepower, and Greece, whose 8.2 million people have been but lightly touched

[3] It is interesting to contrast this idea with the present political and economic alignments in Europe. Politically, the western democracies are distinct from the eastern satellite Communist nations. Economically, three blocs may be easily identified—the six Common Market nations, the seven members of the European Free Trade Association (EFTA), and the nations of the Communist Bloc.

[4] F. Delaisi, *Les Deux Europes; Europe Industrielle et Europe Agricole,* Payot, Paris, 1929.

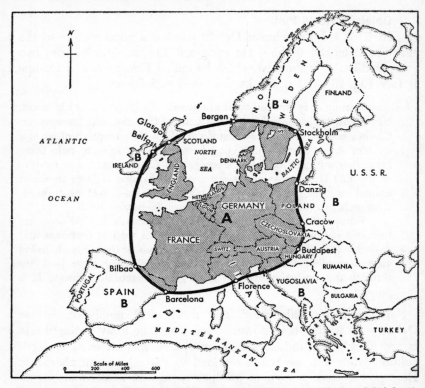

FIGURE 13. Delaisi's Two Europes, Agricultural and Industrial (about 1920)

by the mechanical revolution. The difference in wealth is startling. Thus a nation's position and potentiality reflect its man power multiplied by the coefficient of horsepower. In other words, Europe A in Fig. 13 typifies machine civilization; Europe B, vegetable civilization.

Why did "horsepower" develop to such a great extent in Europe A and not in Europe B? Because only in Europe A were found in usable combination iron and coal, the essentials of the mother industry—the machine industry. Only Europe A, free from the urgent need to obtain immediate returns, possessed the necessary leisure and reserves of capital to build and equip factories. Science, inventing mechanisms, and learning to direct and control machines, and schools to teach this science were found only in Europe A.

Machine Civilization on Other Continents

For some time industrial Europe was busy with itself. The task of creating its machine equipment was stupendous. But then it reached a point of domestic saturation, and, feeling its strength, looked for new worlds to conquer. Thus Europe A became the Mother Europe and created "Europe Beyond the Seas." As Delaisi wrote: "It came to pass that the countless hordes of 'horsepower' soon found themselves lacking space in their Mother Europe. Machinery is condemned to produce in quantity. It must have many markets."

From 1870 to 1890, Europe A, according to Delaisi, thought of modernizing Europe B, especially its Mediterranean and Baltic outskirts; but the social system of the Middle Ages, with its great landed properties on which poor peasants, not far removed from serfdom, carried on agriculture in obsolete ways, was still thriving in Europe B and was not favorable to commercial expansion and industrialization. Moreover, the landed aristocracy dreamed of wars and conquests. Eastern Europe lived in a constant state of threatening war. So Europe A, meaning the owners of surplus capital, turned to young countries beyond the seas. Millions of Europeans left their continent, and European machinery was exchanged for the raw materials and foodstuffs which these emigrants produced. The poor emigrant became a prosperous colonial, and overseas empires— "Europe Beyond the Seas"—sprang up, built by men from Europe B out of and with the aid of the "horsepower" and capital of Europe A. The United States became a new Europe A, Europe A'. For a long time "Europe Beyond the Seas" retained close relations with Mother Europe; but today the tables are turned, and Europe A is dependent on "Europe Beyond the Seas" and must compete with Europe A'. The economic axis is no longer within Europe but somewhere on the ocean.

Delaisi then dealt with the intermediary zone of the tropical lands, "that golden belt of plantations." There climate limits manual labor for the white man, a fact which accounts for the slavery of former days, for forced labor in the form of taxation in Africa, and for the indenture of half-breeds and natives in Latin America today. (Tenant farming sometimes closely resembles these forms of compulsory labor.) The inhabitants of these regions have scarcely any wants and, unless compelled, would not care to produce more than is necessary to satisfy their essential needs.

Regions Little Touched by the Machine

There are also the "sedentary countries" of Asia, with their dense and laboring populations and ancient civilizations. One might think that they would be ready consumers of European goods which they could buy in exchange for cotton, jute, silk, tea, rice, wheat, tobacco, and coffee. But the capitalistic penetration of these vegetable civilizations meets with many obstacles. In China, political differences restrict trade; Japan, industrializing against Europe, is a competitor in Asiatic markets. For numerous reasons the Mohammedan world has not become a good client either. There are many nomadic tribes which have few needs and can export only wool, carpets, and other products of the arid zones in exchange for the few things they want. There are sedentary tribes in oases and along the coasts; these too are generally very poor.

In aggregate numbers the peoples living under vegetable civilizations loom very large. They comprise about three-fourths of the population of the earth, but their productive capacity and hence their consuming and purchasing power are low.

Between the zones settled definitely under either vegetable or machine civilizations lie the pioneer fringes[5]—the experimental zones where, unless the experiments yield negative results, new culture patterns are being woven. These "marginal" zones or frontiers are found in the western United States, in Canada, Australia, South Africa, Siberia, Mongolia, and Manchuria, and in some sections of South America. Their boundary lines shift in response to population pressure, technological progress, the changing availability of capital, a fuller realization of the difficulties which the pioneer has to face, and so forth.

This is a brief sketch of the geographical distribution of resource patterns, culture areas and economic systems. Attention is now directed to the major zones of population density.

[5] See I. Bowman, *The Pioneer Fringe,* Special Publication No. 13, American Geographical Society, New York, 1931.

Changed Reality

Looking back, it is hard to believe that Delaisi's picture could have changed as much as it did. To Delaisi, Russia was a semimysterious eastern appendage of Europe B. It is that no more. It has become a Europe "A," making herculean efforts to deserve that symbol of industrial strength.

In North America petroleum, in the form of both oil and gas, has gained a position rivaling that of coal and has greatly widened the natural basis of industrialization. It has begun to alter the industrial map. North America, while laying claim to Delaisi's title of Europe A', never developed a Europe B'. The division of Europe into A and B rests on historical and political, perhaps even racial, divisions which never materialized in North America. Only in one respect is there a semblance to Europe B which might warrant the name Europe B', and that is dependence on capital. Capital surplus in the United States is still largely generated in the older industrialized areas of the east. The rest of the country, as yet, is dependent on this capital, but decreasingly so. In all other respects the United States is a solid single social economy based on regional specialization, but not split into advanced capitalistic sections and backward feudalistic sections. Above all, the United States is a single political entity in which the benefits of national progress are being shared, not yet equally, to be sure, but in a fashion clearly pointing toward increasing equality.

Perhaps the most profound changes are in the field of ideology. Europe A, the fountainhead of capitalistic ideology, has largely deserted her old faith in laissez faire, has yielded much ground to socialism, and, in spots, to communism. The battle for Europe's soul is on. The Truman Doctrine, Marshall Plan, ERP, ECA, and so forth were weapons used by Europe A' to save Europe A from succumbing to communism. The battlefield stretches around the globe to China, Vietnam, Indonesia, India, Cuba and other parts of Latin America, and to Africa.

This ideological struggle transcends in ultimate significance even the force of technological change and scientific progress. Perhaps it is a race between the two. For technological change and scientific progress hold out a promise of relief from the misery and hopelessness on which communism feeds. The ideological struggle is tragically vital to the future of mankind because the ideology of communism—which has a high-minded ethical, though ineffective, core—is a tool in the hands of a few powerful men who appear to be striving for world conquest through world chaos. Their motives may appear noble to them. The effect of their schemes on mankind is anything but ennobling.

MAJOR RESOURCE PATTERNS

Vegetable vs. Machine Civilization

Whenever there is need of illustrating the two extreme types of civilization, reference is invariably made to monsoon Asia and the United States as examples of vegetable and machine civilization respectively. The contrast is shown diagrammatically in Fig. 14.

The diagram is purely fictitious so far as the sizes of the cubes are concerned. Its claim to verisimilitude lies in the size relationships and in the dynamic interrelation of the three cubes representing the three aspects of resourceship—natural, cultural, and human—or the three factors of production, land, labor, and capital. As was pointed out, capital is the equalizing agent between labor and land. Whichever of the two factors—labor or land—is "long" produces capital to support the "short" factor. In overpopulated areas of monsoon Asia men create rice terraces to render land more productive, to enable the land to support more men. It is a vicious circle which ends in frustration when the entire land area available for use at the *prevailing* state of the arts is occupied and the population has reached the limit of the carrying capacity of the land. The pattern fits perfectly the picture so carefully drawn by Malthus. Population breeds against the means of sustenance. "The Four Horsemen" see to it that death rates keep up with birth rates.

The vegetable civilization of monsoon Asia is uncommonly immobile (see Chapter 5). In the wet rice lands of southern China, a population density of almost 7000 to the square mile is not uncommon. The average for all China is perhaps between 1500 and 2000 inhabitants per square mile of arable land as compared with perhaps 100 for the United States. There is a great lack of mobility in China as compared with western nations, even under communism's stepped-up programs of modernization. While credited with a canal system of some 200,000 miles, most of it is used for

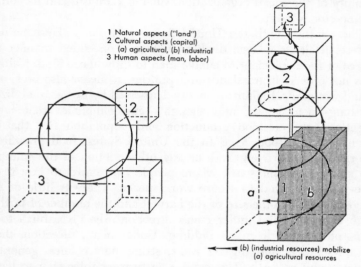

THE RESOURCE PATTERN OF
MONSOON ASIA (COOLIE)

A vicious (Malthusian) cycle in which too many men try to create capital to support too little land to carry more men to try to.....ad infinitum.

THE RESOURCE PATTERN OF THE
UNITED STATES (ROBOT)

An ascending spiral reaching from Nature, manifest in both (a) agriculture- and (b) industry-supporting aspects, creates capital out of the abundance of natural powers to support man, who gradually becomes the director, planner, and aspirer.

1 Natural aspects ("land")
2 Cultural aspects (capital)
   (a) agricultural, (b) industrial
3 Human aspects (man, labor)

◄─────■ (b) (industrial resources) mobilize
          (a) agricultural resources

FIGURE 14. Schematic Presentation of Two Extreme Resource Patterns

irrigation rather than for transportation. Furthermore, many of the vessels are propelled by man power.

Inadequate modern transportation facilities lead to isolation and local self-sufficiency. E. T. Williams aptly referred to China as a nation of village republics—". . . a civilization of small units distributed in accordance with the requirements of a human energy system of land utilization." Even today, the majority of Chinese live in semi-isolated communities struggling to eke out a bare existence. This lack of mobility is aggravated by the necessary consequence of isolation, the lack of cultural standardization, although communism has sought to change this. Differences in language, customs, and mores hinder trade. Being culturally unstandardized, human beings are almost as immobile as the goods themselves.

China historically illustrated the permanence and static nature of vegetable civilizations. Machine civilizations are highly dynamic. The advantages and disadvantages of these characteristics have been discussed earlier. The static nature of a vegetable civilization is institutionally reinforced, often by special mechanisms assuring the continuity of the social organization, such as familism and its corollary, ancestor worship.[6]

The contrast with the United States is striking. Here nature manifests itself in a basic dualism, not in a one-sided manner as a source of food sufficient to enable man to grow more food. Nature means not only rich grasslands and prairies; it means also ores, oil, gas, and waterfalls. Inanimate energy, harnessed by metals, mobilizes everything—men, goods, and thoughts—and eliminates that fatal connection between food production and population size that is the curse of monsoon Asia. In the United States, food grown in California moves to New York or any other section of the country or to any part of the earth where people can afford to buy it or where it can be used to secure world peace. There is little or no connection between the size of the harvest and the number of births. Nature creates capital under man's direction. She gives birth to a billion robots that do man's bidding. Under man's direction, they build skyscrapers and dig oil wells, string power lines, generate electricity, and so forth. This capital, in turn, enables man to have higher living standards, to enjoy more leisure, to safeguard his health, to prolong his life span—in short, to yield real wealth. (See Fig. 14.)

While the monsoonia pattern resembles a circle—a vicious circle—the pattern of horsepower land, as one may call the United States—resembles an ascending spiral. As it reaches loftier heights, it becomes thinner. It is like a high pyramid built on a broad base but so tall that it is dangerously exposed to high winds. It is a bold structure, but the towering height is not without its risks. Vegetable civilization is like a giant squatting on the ground in sodden safety.

Resource Patterns in the United States

Exclusive of her noncontiguous territories—Alaska, Puerto Rico, Hawaii, and the Virgin Islands—the United States covers an area of almost three million square miles—about 6 percent of the land

---

[6] D. H. Kulp, II, "Chinese Continuity," *Annals of the American Academy of Political and Social Science,* November, 1930, pp. 18 ff.

area of the earth—a massive continent which differs strikingly from Europe, a peninsula of Eurasia. Within this huge territory is found an unparalleled variety of climatic, soil, topographical, and geological conditions. The number of commercially important crops is unsurpassed anywhere. Where else are such expansive cotton, corn, and wheat areas—to name only the three leading crops—assembled under such favorable producing conditions within the confines of a single political entity? Moreover, almost one-sixth of this area is underlaid with coal which ranges from the poorest lignite to the finest steam coal and anthracite. The coal is ideally supplemented by petroleum, as in California, Texas, and Oklahoma, and by water power throughout the entire western third, in the extreme Northeast, and in the Southeast. No region of comparable size can boast of an array of power resources which, in advantageous arrangement and availability, can compare with those of the United States.

Europe also has valuable energy resources; but until a united Europe, of which the EEC (or European Economic Community) may be a beginning, arises from the mess of political provincialism and petty rivalries which put innumerable obstacles in the path of progress, these resources will remain insufficiently coördinated. Political boundaries play a part of ominous importance on a continent filled with suspicion and fear, and all too often they interfere with a rational utilization of nature's wealth. Thus the United States is strong because of her excellent energy resources, but she is stronger still because of the historical development which united the separate states. America too has her squabbles—witness the fierce struggle over civil rights—but as yet these schisms are relatively harmless compared with the events which robbed Silesia of half her value and tore the Ruhr-Lorraine unit into opposing halves.

No other continent possesses energy resources comparable in extent, variety, and availability to those of Europe and America. The same holds true of the machine resources. With few exceptions, what deficiencies there are can be made good through financial control over foreign deposits.

The United States is a country of vast continental expanse, at one and the same time the most highly mineralized area and the largest producer of vegetable and animal products. But wealth arouses the envy of the less fortunate, and invites attack. Many an empire of the past has succumbed in that way. But here again nature favors the United States beyond belief. On the east and west, the wide expanse of the Atlantic and Pacific; to the north, a prosperous neighbor, a blood relation. No Verdun or Belfort marks that "international line," grim reminders of strange "neighborliness." The situation to the south had not aroused fears, unless it be the fear that superior strength invites abuse, until the Cuban crisis.

If security and abundance are prerequisites of a rich material civilization, it is not surprising to find its highest development in North America, north of the Rio Grande. While other continents were diverted by periodic warfare or fear of it, until recently the United States and her friendly neighbor to the north were able to concentrate single-mindedly on the business of wealth creation.

Unfortunately the situation is deteriorating. More and more, North America is being drawn into the whirlpool of world politics; the United States is being compelled to give more and more attention to military plans and is progressively being exposed to possible enemy attack. It started with the submarine and the airplane, which turned oceans into mere moats. It became worse when in World War II western Europe came close to being knocked out and the Soviet Union gained the stature of a Super Power. The conquest of China by the communists made the situation even more critical. And the knowledge of atomic explosions in the Soviet Union and of that nation's achievements in space went far to remove from North America the last vestige of a once superior position of security. What has been true of Europe for half a century or longer is now happening in North America. Industries are being moved to safer locations, some even underground, and people are being moved in response to strategic requirements. The old freedom of pursuing economic aims undisturbed by military considerations is waning rapidly. It will in time be reflected in still heavier tax burdens and in higher costs of production brought on by departures from economic rationality.

Yet, all these changes are relative. If the situation is deteriorating in North America, it is deteriorating even more rapidly elsewhere, and a certain margin of advantage may long remain. Moreover, this continent should for long feel the benefit of the momentum gained from its earlier superiority. Above all, North America's unique endowment with natural assets, as well as the blessings of the American way of life, may at least in part offset the unfavorable developments in recent global history.

From natural assets we now turn to institutions, and again an international comparison proves helpful. This time America and Europe are used for this purpose. Both regions were settled by the white man. Racially the populations of the two continents have much in common. Moreover, there has been a constant interchange of experience. But the culture patterns as revealed in the institutions and in particular in the attitude toward resources are markedly different in the two continents. This calls for an explanation.

Without wishing to imply that such complex questions can be answered by a single argument, it seems that one cause, more than any other, accounts for this difference between the two continents, namely, the fact that the white man settled most of Europe before, and most of America after, the mechanical revolution. He settled much of Europe with the broadax and sweat, much of America with railroads and steam. The European settlement spread at a snail's pace, progress was slow, the tools were primitive, and weak man was only inadequately supported by work animals and beasts of burden. After the Appalachian Mountains ceased to be the western boundary, the conquest of the North American continent was a race; with the aid of steam man could in a day settle a territory which formerly could hardly have been subdued in a decade.

This difference in manner and above all in tempo, perhaps more than any other single fact, accounts for the striking differences which exist today between Europe and America. In the first place, Europeans developed their attitudes, customs, and institutions in times of relative isolation. The result is *regional particularism*. Differences of languages developed; the customs of one town seemed strange to its neighbors only a few miles away. When the railroad finally came, these differences were so deeply ingrained that narrow nationalism, fanned by bitter memories of strife, replaced the former particularism. The past therefore weighs heavily upon the minds of Europeans. They are "time people"; they judge the present and the future in the light of past events. Precedent and tradition still largely govern the mind. Man thinks and acts because his medieval ancestor still survives in him. The driver of today has to listen to the back-seat driver of the past.

Contrast this situation with that existing in the United States. In general, American traditions can be traced to only a minority of those who settled the New World. Most emigrants had to unlearn their own traditions; they had to live in the present and for the future only. The present made such demands on the strength of the bold adventurer and, in return, held out such rewards for effort that it became of transcending importance in shaping the new national character and weaving the new culture pattern. The immediate environment spoke louder than the soft voice of past memories. In contrast to the "time people" of Europe, the North Americans, to a high degree, are "place people," that is to say, people whose attitudes are largely determined by the physical environment through the occupation it forces upon them. The absence of strong local traditions permits widespread homogeneity in customs and the outlook on life.

But that is not all. Possibly the greatest difference between the two continents is to be found in the greater and more varied endowment in natural assets in North America and the resulting fact that a larger share of resources is available for each man, woman, and child. If a region is opened up slowly, step by step, over a long period of time, the amount of natural wealth available at any one time is not apt to be very large. If, on the other hand, a huge continent, endowed with every variety of nature's gifts, is settled with impetuous vigor, the amount of resources available for the use of each generation is infinitely greater. The historical development of Europe, therefore, has been marked by a moderate availability of natural wealth. This is in striking contrast to the almost overwhelming abundance found in this country. The creeping exploitation of European resources rendered quite difficult the production of a surplus over consumption; the process of capital accumulation was bound to be both slow and painful.

On the other hand, the whirlwind exploitation which is taking place on this continent greatly facilitates the accumulation of surplus capital. It proceeds rapidly and, particularly of late, almost painlessly. Such a difference is bound to reflect upon the economic system in general and on the attitude toward natural resources in particular. It is dangerous to generalize, but one would be inclined to ascribe to this difference in the mode of settlement a certain shortsighted economy frequently found in Europe, and a certain shortsighted wastefulness characteristic of America. How this difference in opportunities and task has necessitated a different development of technological arts in America and Europe was pointed out in Chapter 3.

America, an Experiment in Transportation

Whether this mechanization of production has brought about a state of optimum population, an ideal man-land ratio, (see Chapter 8) cannot be concluded with any degree of certainty. For some 190 million people to inhabit a country of continental expanse which could well support many more not only means that there are more resources available per capita than on a continent of much smaller size; it also implies a handicap of space. It is conceivable that, next to institutional maladjustments, her excessive space is the greatest weakness of the resource position of the United States.

This is a thought which to many appears rather strange. Space—abundance of space—has its glorious advantages. It develops vision, widens the horizon, allows freedom of motion, and helps in many other ways. But there is no gainsaying that an excess of space is one of the greatest luxuries, one of the most expensive possessions of which a country may boast. One has only to imagine a country of continental expanse which consists of an enormous desert surrounded by a narrow margin of productive land—some people think of Australia in this way. The Australians would probably be much better off if their resources were concentrated upon a very much smaller area. The pulse of economic and social life would beat quicker, and much effort, time, and wealth could be saved if short direct connections could replace the circuitous journeys necessary at present.

North America is not as extreme a case of "elephantiasis" as Australia. And yet one wonders whether, at times, we do not show symptoms of the same trouble. The United States has been called an experiment in transportation. What does this mean? Paraphrasing Lincoln, we might say that it means an experiment to determine whether a nation so conceived in continental expanse can long survive. Lincoln referred to a political experiment; but the United States is also an economic experiment. Lincoln referred to the strain which experiments in political institutions place upon a democracy. Here, we refer to the strain which an experiment in economic institutions places upon natural and material resources. Railroads and highways, automobiles and pipelines, telephones and power transmission lines are the means of overcoming the space handicap and of creating prosperity in spite of excessive space. In many cases at least, the automobile is not a sign of excessive prosperity but a means of overcoming America's greatest handicap, the excess of space.

Coal mines may lie a thousand miles from the iron ore. Food is grown a thousand miles and more away from the point of consumption. The magnificent transportation facilities which bring the ore to the coal or the food to the consumer are not assets in the ordinary sense of the word; they are the means by which we overcome the tremendous handicaps placed in our way by the excess of space. To be sure, without our unexcelled transportation system we would be paralyzed. To understand the true function of a transportation system in our economic system, we must not compare the present situation with one in which we have no means of transportation; we must visualize ourselves living on a continent perhaps one-third the size, containing within its borders the same natural wealth which we command today, but excluding the great barren spaces which separate the productive areas today and whose conquest lays such a heavy burden upon our economic system. That is the meaning of the phrase: America, an experiment in transportation.[7]

The disproportionately heavy burden which transportation places upon our economic system may indicate that we are still below the optimum point. Since the construction of transportation facilities—railroads, bridges, stations, warehouses, highways, automobiles, buses, trucks, etc.—requires a great deal of iron and steel and other machine resources as well as a considerable amount of power resources, and since the operation of this transportation sys-

[7] George Otis Smith, formerly Director of the United States Geological Survey, and Chairman of the Federal Power Commission, speaking before the International Railway Fuel Association on May 10, 1927, developed this idea in admirable fashion. He gave his speech the telling title "What Price Distance?" This same idea is developed in an interesting manner by M. M. Knight, "Water and the Course of Empire in North Africa," *Quarterly Journal of Economics*, November, 1928.

The huge transportation apparatus is part of John Meynard Keynes' famous "cake" in the growth of which he saw the central object of worship of the capitalistic religion of progress, and which he considered the enchanted "cake" which neither the workers that made it nor the men that owned it could ever eat.

tem requires some machine resources for upkeep and an enormous amount of energy resources for daily use, the per capita expenditure of machine and energy resources in this country assumes a new meaning.

One may be inclined to argue that it does not make any difference to a laborer whether he earns his living building a railroad bridge or making a refrigerator. In other words, the production of transportation facilities implies that hundreds of thousands, if not millions, of people are earning their living in the process. But the point is this: if the same millions could earn their living making consumers' goods rather than production goods such as steel rails and railroad bridges, the country as a whole would be still better off, provided we accept per capita intake of consumers' goods as an adequate criterion of national well-being. Nobody would suggest that in times of normal business activity the American people are not well off in a material sense. It would be foolish to deny this prosperity when innumerable items of evidence stare the observer in the face. Normally, America may be considered prosperous, the per capita income of material consumers' goods probably being greater than anywhere else in the world. This, however, should not blind us to the truth.

It would be a mistake to conclude from the foregoing discussion that density of population is the only remedy for excessive space and the consequent excessive expenditure for transportation. A look at New York City will readily convince one that this cannot be so. Excessive population density necessitates heavy transportation expenditure at least as much as does excessive sparsity, though for different reasons. It is not maximum density but optimum density which can solve the problem. Since excessive space is the one great handicap under which North America labors, and since that handicap can be neutralized through improved transportation and communication, it follows that every improvement of the arts, every invention and every discovery which make transportation and communication more efficient and therefore cheaper, mean most to that country which is most dependent on efficient transportation.[8]

To repeat, the United States is an experiment in transportation,

---

[8] This discussion of transportation could well be extended to include many other services which are direct or indirect corollaries of an exchange economy of continental expanse. Reference is made to marketing, advertising, banking, insurance, and all other facilitating activities.

and the more efficient transportation is, the more that experiment is apt to succeed. Every increase in transportation efficiency means a step forward toward optimum density. In a country where friction can be abolished and an ounce of coal can move a ton of freight, where tare is reduced to a minimum, the optimum population lies at a much lower point on the population density scale than in a country where wheelbarrows and jinrikishas are the principal means of transportation. The more we use radios, wireless telegraphy, and rubber-tired wheels running on ball bearings and on concrete roads, the closer we come to the ideal transportation condition and the lower moves the point of optimum population on the density scale. In fact, it is not at all impossible that the rapid strides made in the realm of transportation and communication during the past two or three decades go further to explain American prosperity than almost any other single factor. The greater efficiency in electric power production and transmission which relieved the pressure on coal mining and on railroad transportation, the improvement in gasoline production, inventions in the field of wireless telegraphy, in telephony and television, all have contributed toward lowering the optimum point. The triumph of the robot and the conquest of space solve the two problems which alone stood in the way of American prosperity—*labor scarcity* and *excess of space*. As far as America's natural position is concerned, little remains to be desired except that man's wisdom be commensurate to the opportunity. It would seem rash to assume that this condition has as yet been met.

THE RESOURCE HIERARCHY OF MODERN WORLD ECONOMY

The Mechanical Revolution the Great Divide of Mankind

The mechanical revolution has shifted the center of gravity from land or soil—food-producing, man-supporting soil—to inanimate energy, to horsepower, to robots. Wealth and strength depend not primarily on the size of armies or the number of coolies, but on control over the inanimate energies of nature through the power-driven machine and through science. The two major powers of the world today—the United States and the Soviet Union—are leaders in the output of energy-yielding fuels and energy-harnessing steel. A united western Europe will be a powerful political unit. It will rank high in the aggregate output of coal and iron. There are no great industrial nations in the southern hemisphere. There are no great powers in the southern hemisphere. When Japan coveted the glory of becoming a great power she pushed the exploration of her limited domestic iron and coal reserves to the utmost and strove to supplement them in every conceivable way. It looks as if the feudalism of the twentieth century was the feudalism of horsepower as the ancient feudalism had been a feudalism of man power and man-power-supporting land.

Thus, political power seems to be associated in some way with industrialization, the branch of production that relies on inanimate energy. Agrarian and pastoral countries are weak countries politically. As a rule they are also poor countries. Horsepower in the modern world appears as the key not only to power but also to wealth. When agriculture was left to fight things out with industry in the open market, agriculture seemed to get the worst of the bargain. Industrial countries enjoyed stronger bargaining positions than did agrarian countries. More often than not, industries, in one way or another, to a greater or lesser extent, enjoyed the advantage of closer control over output while agriculture remained bound to the irresistible rhythm of nature. Until government intervened on the side of the weak to assure a better balance of bargaining power, agriculture seemed to grow poorer and industry richer. Cities became notorious centers of wealth, whereas the open country was neglected and backward.

Cities throve not only as centers of industry, but as centers of commerce as well. They became the great nodal points where the controls over tertiary activities such as trade, finance, insurance, professional work, education, governmental activities were centered. The great organized exchanges became symbols of these concentrations of invisible powers, as did the palatial head offices of the great corporations from which wires and wireless reach to the far corners of the earth.

From Economic Egalitarianism to Hierarchy

More and more the economic order took on the appearance of a vast hierarchy, i.e., a structure of staggered control, a structure resting on a huge basis of raw-material production with power centered in the heavy industries and the leading banks. The world economy in general, as well as individual national economies, seemed to divide more and more into active and passive elements. The right to active participation in economic control seems to spring from the capacity to earn profits and accumulate surplus; this in turn seems associated with the ability to apply science and the power-driven machine generally through corporate structures. Now and then a country or region that produced agricultural raw materials would find itself in an exceptionally favorable market position and for a while it would accumulate credit. But sooner or later the market would turn against it and the credit would be dissipated in a spree of luxury buying or in desperate efforts to industrialize. At times vast credits proved uncollectible.

In the procurement of raw materials the powers possessed of active control have a choice of policy. They may acquire the source of raw materials or they may prefer to have others continue as independent producers. By and large, the choice of policy between absorption of the source itself and purchase from the dependent source seems to be affected if not determined by the nature of the material involved. In general, mineral raw materials are absorbed into the corporate structure through ownership of mines, whereas agricultural products, especially the great staples such as wheat, corn, rye, potatoes, cotton, etc., are allowed to remain the product of the independent grower. An exception to this is certain perennial crops such as rubber, sugar cane, and bananas, which come under corporate control and management.

The hierarchical structure of the modern world economy may be expressed diagrammatically, as shown in Fig. 15.[9] The two "fields of force," MN and OP, it will be noted, represent the alternative policies of "absorption" or "acquisition" by purchase discussed above. When industries in the power center decide on the second alternative, national policy may undertake to influence the market position in their favor.

In the modern world there are several "power centers." Moscow would undoubtedly be one, New York-Washington would be another. London and Paris are striving valiantly to hold on to their respective peaks.

Such power centers differ in vital respects. Thus in Soviet Russia

[9] This diagram was first published in Erich W. Zimmermann, "The Resource Hierarchy in Modern World Economy," *Weltwirtschaftliches Archiv*, April, 1931.

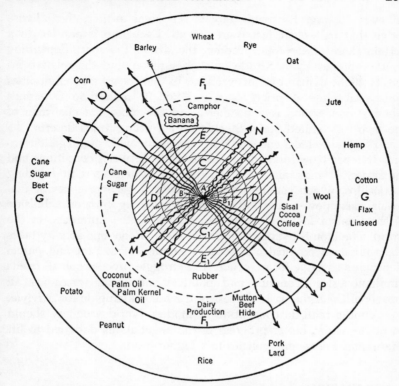

FIGURE 15. The Resource Hierarchy of Modern World Economy

the power of government and of business control is combined in the Politburo. In the United States the relationship of government and business is highly complex, at times the government backing big business in its raw-material procurement efforts, and at other times acting as arbiter between big business and little business, big business and farmers, big business and consumers, etc. The difference is that between a totalitarian state and a democracy. These are two extremes; between them there are many gradations.

The hierarchical conception of the modern world economy here propounded is quite different from that presented in traditional texts on international trade theory. The traditional approach is atomistic. It thinks of the world as a single market in which two billion and more human beings meet as buyers and sellers, all on an even footing. Economic law is the great arbiter, the all-wise judge that metes out just shares to all. Each one is entitled to a certain share of the total product, the size of the share depending on the comparative aptitude of each supplier and the relative intensity of the demand for his product. In that theory all commodities possess absolute *a priori* comparability. It makes no difference whether one person is a goatherd and the other the chairman of the board of United States Steel; each according to his deserts.

The hierarchical concept is irreconcilable with such egalitarianism. It recognizes fundamental differences between conditions and industries. It maintains that whether one is engaged in building battleships, which can be done only with huge aggregates of materials, man power, and equipment, or growing corn on a hillside of the Central Plateau of Mexico, makes all the difference in the world. The atomistic approach is unrealistic. Economic activity takes place not in a political and social vacuum, but as part and parcel of people's struggle for existence. The struggle proceeds on all fronts simultaneously. Economic and political and social forces are all aspects of the same basic process of the human struggle for survival.

A more realistic conception of modern world economy should go far to assure better progress in the negotiations designed to lift international economic policies to a higher level.

BIBLIOGRAPHY

Alexander, John W., *Economic Geography*, Englewood Cliffs, N.J.: Prentice-Hall, Inc., 1963.

Benoit, Emile, *Europe at Sixes and Sevens*, New York: Columbia University Press, 1961.

Clark, Colin, *The Common Market and British Trade*, New York: Frederick A. Praeger, Inc., 1962.

Clark, Colin, *The Real Productivity of Soviet Russia*, Washington, D.C.: United States Government Printing Office, 1961.

Deniau, Jean Francois, *The Common Market*, New York: Frederick A. Praeger, Inc., 1960.

Dewhurst, J. Frederick, *America's Needs and Resources, A New Survey*, New York: Twentieth Century Fund, 1955.

Dewhurst, J. Frederick, John O. Coppock, P. Lamartine Yates, and associates, *Europe's Needs and Resources,* New York: Twentieth Century Fund, 1961.

Holzman, Franklyn D., *Readings on the Soviet Economy,* Chicago: Rand McNally & Company, 1962.

Huxley, Aldous, *Brave New World,* New York: Harper & Row, Publishers, Inc., 1932.

Huxley, Aldous, *Brave New World Revisited,* New York: Harper & Row, Publishers, Inc., 1958.

James, Preston E., *Latin America,* New York: The Odyssey Press, 1959.

Landsberg, Hans H., Leonard L. Fischman, and Joseph L. Fisher, *Resources in America's Future,* Baltimore: The Johns Hopkins Press (for Resources for the Future), 1963.

Myrdal, Gunnar, *Challenge to Affluence,* New York: Pantheon Books, 1963.

Spengler, Joseph J. (Ed.), *Natural Resources and Economic Growth,* Washington, D.C.: Resources for the Future, Inc., 1961.

Thoman, Richard S., *The Geography of Economic Activity,* New York: The McGraw-Hill Book Company, Inc., 1962.

Tinbergen, Jan, *Shaping the World Economy,* New York: Twentieth Century Fund, 1962.

INDEX

70   7

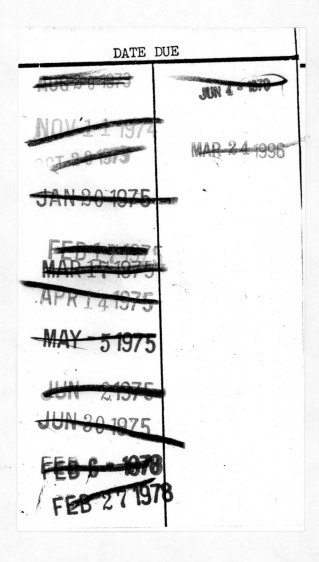